TEACHER'S GUIDE

Connected  Mathematics2™

Accentuate the Negative

Integers and Rational Numbers

Glenda Lappan
James T. Fey
William M. Fitzgerald
Susan N. Friel
Elizabeth Difanis Phillips

PEARSON

Boston, Massachusetts · Glenview, Illinois · Shoreview, Minnesota · Upper Saddle River, New Jersey

Connected Mathematics™ was developed at Michigan State University with financial support from the Michigan State University Office of the Provost, Computing and Technology, and the College of Natural Science.

 This material is based upon work supported by the National Science Foundation under Grant No. MDR 9150217 and Grant No. ESI 9986372. Opinions expressed are those of the authors and not necessarily those of the Foundation.

The Michigan State University authors and administration have agreed that all MSU royalties arising from this publication will be devoted to purposes supported by the Department of Mathematics and the MSU Mathematics Enrichment Fund.

13-digit ISBN 978-0-13-366195-8
10-digit ISBN 0-13-366195-4
1 2 3 4 5 6 7 8 9 10   11 10 09 08

Authors of Connected Mathematics

(from left to right) Glenda Lappan, Betty Phillips, Susan Friel, Bill Fitzgerald, Jim Fey

Glenda Lappan is a University Distinguished Professor in the Department of Mathematics at Michigan State University. Her research and development interests are in the connected areas of students' learning of mathematics and mathematics teachers' professional growth and change related to the development and enactment of K–12 curriculum materials.

James T. Fey is a Professor of Curriculum and Instruction and Mathematics at the University of Maryland. His consistent professional interest has been development and research focused on curriculum materials that engage middle and high school students in problem-based collaborative investigations of mathematical ideas and their applications.

William M. Fitzgerald (*Deceased*) was a Professor in the Department of Mathematics at Michigan State University. His early research was on the use of concrete materials in supporting student learning and led to the development of teaching materials for laboratory environments. Later he helped develop a teaching model to support student experimentation with mathematics.

Susan N. Friel is a Professor of Mathematics Education in the School of Education at the University of North Carolina at Chapel Hill. Her research interests focus on statistics education for middle-grade students and, more broadly, on teachers' professional development and growth in teaching mathematics K–8.

Elizabeth Difanis Phillips is a Senior Academic Specialist in the Mathematics Department of Michigan State University. She is interested in teaching and learning mathematics for both teachers and students. These interests have led to curriculum and professional development projects at the middle school and high school levels, as well as projects related to the teaching and learning of algebra across the grades.

CMP2 Development Staff

Teacher Collaborator in Residence
Yvonne Grant
Michigan State University

Administrative Assistant
Judith Martus Miller
Michigan State University

Production and Field Site Manager
Lisa Keller
Michigan State University

Technical and Editorial Support
Brin Keller, Peter Lappan, Jim Laser,
Michael Masterson, Stacey Miceli

Assessment Team

June Bailey and **Debra Sobko** (Apollo Middle School, Rochester, New York), **George Bright** (University of North Carolina, Greensboro), **Gwen Ranzau Campbell** (Sunrise Park Middle School, White Bear Lake, Minnesota), **Holly DeRosia, Kathy Dole,** and **Teri Keusch** (Portland Middle School, Portland, Michigan), **Mary Beth Schmitt** (Traverse City East Junior High School, Traverse City, Michigan), **Genni Steele** (Central Middle School, White Bear Lake, Minnesota), **Jacqueline Stewart** (Okemos, Michigan), **Elizabeth Tye** (Magnolia Junior High School, Magnolia, Arkansas)

Development Assistants

At Lansing Community College *Undergraduate Assistant:* **James Brinegar**

At Michigan State University *Graduate Assistants:* **Dawn Berk, Emily Bouck, Bulent Buyukbozkirli, Kuo-Liang Chang, Christopher Danielson, Srinivasa Dharmavaram, Deb Johanning, Wesley Kretzschmar, Kelly Rivette, Sarah Sword, Tat Ming Sze, Marie Turini, Jeffrey Wanko;** *Undergraduate Assistants:* **Daniel Briggs, Jeffrey Chapin, Jade Corsé, Elisha Hardy, Alisha Harold, Elizabeth Keusch, Julia Letoutchaia, Karen Loeffler, Brian Oliver, Carl Oliver, Evonne Pedawi, Lauren Rebrovich**

At the University of Maryland *Graduate Assistants:* **Kim Harris Bethea, Kara Karch**

At the University of North Carolina (Chapel Hill) *Graduate Assistants:* **Mark Ellis, Trista Stearns;** *Undergraduate Assistant:* **Daniel Smith**

Advisory Board for CMP2

Thomas Banchoff
Professor of Mathematics
Brown University
Providence, Rhode Island

Anne Bartel
Mathematics Coordinator
Minneapolis Public Schools
Minneapolis, Minnesota

Hyman Bass
Professor of Mathematics
University of Michigan
Ann Arbor, Michigan

Joan Ferrini-Mundy
Associate Dean of the College of
Natural Science; Professor
Michigan State University
East Lansing, Michigan

James Hiebert
Professor
University of Delaware
Newark, Delaware

Susan Hudson Hull
Charles A. Dana Center
University of Texas
Austin, Texas

Michele Luke
Mathematics Curriculum
Coordinator
West Junior High
Minnetonka, Minnesota

Kay McClain
Assistant Professor of
Mathematics Education
Vanderbilt University
Nashville, Tennessee

Edward Silver
Professor; Chair of Educational
Studies
University of Michigan
Ann Arbor, Michigan

Judith Sowder
Professor Emerita
San Diego State University
San Diego, California

Lisa Usher
Mathematics Resource Teacher
California Academy of
Mathematics and Science
San Pedro, California

Field Test Sites for CMP2

During the development of the revised edition of *Connected Mathematics* (CMP2), more than 100 classroom teachers have field-tested materials at 49 school sites in 12 states and the District of Columbia. This classroom testing occurred over three academic years (2001 through 2004), allowing careful study of the effectiveness of each of the 24 units that comprise the program. A special thanks to the students and teachers at these pilot schools.

Arkansas
Magnolia Public Schools
Kittena Bell*, Judith Trowell*; *Central Elementary School:* Maxine Broom, Betty Eddy, Tiffany Fallin, Bonnie Flurry, Carolyn Monk, Elizabeth Tye; *Magnolia Junior High School:* Monique Bryan, Ginger Cook, David Graham, Shelby Lamkin

Colorado
Boulder Public Schools
Nevin Platt Middle School: Judith Koenig

St. Vrain Valley School District, Longmont
Westview Middle School: Colleen Beyer, Kitty Canupp, Ellie Decker*, Peggy McCarthy, Tanya deNobrega, Cindy Payne, Ericka Pilon, Andrew Roberts

District of Columbia
Capitol Hill Day School: Ann Lawrence

Georgia
University of Georgia, Athens
Brad Findell

Madison Public Schools
Morgan County Middle School: Renee Burgdorf, Lynn Harris, Nancy Kurtz, Carolyn Stewart

Maine
Falmouth Public Schools
Falmouth Middle School: Donna Erikson, Joyce Hebert, Paula Hodgkins, Rick Hogan, David Legere, Cynthia Martin, Barbara Stiles, Shawn Towle*

Michigan
Portland Public Schools
Portland Middle School: Mark Braun, Holly DeRosia, Kathy Dole*, Angie Foote, Teri Keusch, Tammi Wardwell

Traverse City Area Public Schools
Bertha Vos Elementary: Kristin Sak; *Central Grade School:* Michelle Clark; Jody Meyers; *Eastern Elementary:* Karrie Tufts; *Interlochen Elementary:* Mary McGee-Cullen; *Long Lake Elementary:* Julie Faulkner*, Charlie Maxbauer, Katherine Sleder; *Norris Elementary:* Hope Slanaker; *Oak Park Elementary:* Jessica Steed; *Traverse Heights Elementary:* Jennifer Wolfert; *Westwoods Elementary:* Nancy Conn; *Old Mission Peninsula School:* Deb Larimer; *Traverse City East Junior High:* Ivanka Berkshire, Ruthanne Kladder, Jan Palkowski, Jane Peterson, Mary Beth Schmitt; *Traverse City West Junior High:* Dan Fouch*, Ray Fouch

Sturgis Public Schools
Sturgis Middle School: Ellen Eisele

Minnesota
Burnsville School District 191
Hidden Valley Elementary: Stephanie Cin, Jane McDevitt

Hopkins School District 270
Alice Smith Elementary: Sandra Cowing, Kathleen Gustafson, Martha Mason, Scott Stillman; *Eisenhower Elementary:* Chad Bellig, Patrick Berger, Nancy Glades, Kye Johnson, Shane Wasserman, Victoria Wilson; *Gatewood Elementary:* Sarah Ham, Julie Kloos, Janine Pung, Larry Wade; *Glen Lake Elementary:* Jacqueline Cramer, Kathy Hering, Cecelia Morris, Robb Trenda; *Katherine Curren Elementary:* Diane Bancroft, Sue DeWit, John Wilson; *L. H. Tanglen Elementary:* Kevin Athmann, Lisa Becker, Mary LaBelle, Kathy Rezac, Roberta Severson; *Meadowbrook Elementary:* Jan Gauger, Hildy Shank, Jessica Zimmerman; *North Junior High:* Laurel Hahn, Kristin Lee, Jodi Markuson, Bruce Mestemacher, Laurel Miller, Bonnie Rinker, Jeannine Salzer, Sarah Shafer, Cam Stottler; *West Junior High:* Alicia Beebe, Kristie Earl, Nobu Fujii, Pam Georgetti, Susan Gilbert, Regina Nelson Johnson, Debra Lindstrom, Michele Luke*, Jon Sorensen

Minneapolis School District 1
Ann Sullivan K–8 School: Bronwyn Collins; Anne Bartel* (Curriculum and Instruction Office)

Wayzata School District 284
Central Middle School: Sarajane Myers, Dan Nielsen, Tanya Ravnholdt

White Bear Lake School District 624
Central Middle School: Amy Jorgenson, Michelle Reich, Brenda Sammon

New York
New York City Public Schools
IS 89: Yelena Aynbinder, Chi-Man Ng, Nina Rapaport, Joel Spengler, Phyllis Tam*, Brent Wyso; *Wagner Middle School:* Jason Appel, Intissar Fernandez, Yee Gee Get, Richard Goldstein, Irving Marcus, Sue Norton, Bernadita Owens, Jennifer Rehn*, Kevin Yuhas

---

* indicates a Field Test Site Coordinator

Ohio

Talawanda School District, Oxford
Talawanda Middle School: Teresa Abrams, Larry Brock, Heather Brosey, Julie Churchman, Monna Even, Karen Fitch, Bob George, Amanda Klee, Pat Meade, Sandy Montgomery, Barbara Sherman, Lauren Steidl

Miami University
Jeffrey Wanko*

Springfield Public Schools
Rockway School: Jim Mamer

Pennsylvania

Pittsburgh Public Schools
Kenneth Labuskes, Marianne O'Connor, Mary Lynn Raith*; *Arthur J. Rooney Middle School:* David Hairston, Stamatina Mousetis, Alfredo Zangaro; *Frick International Studies Academy:* Suzanne Berry, Janet Falkowski, Constance Finseth, Romika Hodge, Frank Machi; *Reizenstein Middle School:* Jeff Baldwin, James Brautigam, Lorena Burnett, Glen Cobbett, Michael Jordan, Margaret Lazur, Tamar McPherson, Melissa Munnell, Holly Neely, Ingrid Reed, Dennis Reft

Texas

Austin Independent School District
Bedichek Middle School: Lisa Brown, Jennifer Glasscock, Vicki Massey

El Paso Independent School District
Cordova Middle School: Armando Aguirre, Anneliesa Durkes, Sylvia Guzman, Pat Holguin*, William Holguin, Nancy Nava, Laura Orozco, Michelle Peña, Roberta Rosen, Patsy Smith, Jeremy Wolf

Plano Independent School District
Patt Henry, James Wohlgehagen*; *Frankford Middle School:* Mandy Baker, Cheryl Butsch, Amy Dudley, Betsy Eshelman, Janet Greene, Cort Haynes, Kathy Letchworth, Kay Marshall, Kelly McCants, Amy Reck, Judy Scott, Syndy Snyder, Lisa Wang; *Wilson Middle School:* Darcie Bane, Amanda Bedenko, Whitney Evans, Tonelli Hatley, Sarah (Becky) Higgs, Kelly Johnston, Rebecca McElligott, Kay Neuse, Cheri Slocum, Kelli Straight

Washington

Evergreen School District
Shahala Middle School: Nicole Abrahamsen, Terry Coon*, Carey Doyle, Sheryl Drechsler, George Gemma, Gina Helland, Amy Hilario, Darla Lidyard, Sean McCarthy, Tilly Meyer, Willow Nuewelt, Todd Parsons, Brian Pederson, Stan Posey, Shawn Scott, Craig Sjoberg, Lynette Sundstrom, Charles Switzer, Luke Youngblood

Wisconsin

Beaver Dam Unified School District
Beaver Dam Middle School: Jim Braemer, Jeanne Frick, Jessica Greatens, Barbara Link, Dennis McCormick, Karen Michels, Nancy Nichols*, Nancy Palm, Shelly Stelsel, Susan Wiggins

* indicates a Field Test Site Coordinator

Reviews of CMP to Guide Development of CMP2

Before writing for CMP2 began or field tests were conducted, the first edition of *Connected Mathematics* was submitted to the mathematics faculties of school districts from many parts of the country and to 80 individual reviewers for extensive comments.

School District Survey Reviews of CMP

Arizona
Madison School District #38 (Phoenix)

Arkansas
Cabot School District, Little Rock School District, Magnolia School District

California
Los Angeles Unified School District

Colorado
St. Vrain Valley School District (Longmont)

Florida
Leon County Schools (Tallahassee)

Illinois
School District #21 (Wheeling)

Indiana
Joseph L. Block Junior High (East Chicago)

Kentucky
Fayette County Public Schools (Lexington)

Maine
Selection of Schools

Massachusetts
Selection of Schools

Michigan
Sparta Area Schools

Minnesota
Hopkins School District

Texas
Austin Independent School District, The El Paso Collaborative for Academic Excellence, Plano Independent School District

Wisconsin
Platteville Middle School

Individual Reviewers of CMP

Arkansas
Deborah Cramer; Robby Frizzell *(Taylor)*; Lowell Lynde *(University of Arkansas, Monticello)*; Leigh Manzer *(Norfork)*; Lynne Roberts *(Emerson High School, Emerson)*; Tony Timms *(Cabot Public Schools)*; Judith Trowell *(Arkansas Department of Higher Education)*

California
José Alcantar *(Gilroy)*; Eugenie Belcher *(Gilroy)*; Marian Pasternack *(Lowman M. S. T. Center, North Hollywood)*; Susana Pezoa *(San Jose)*; Todd Rabusin *(Hollister)*; Margaret Siegfried *(Ocala Middle School, San Jose)*; Polly Underwood *(Ocala Middle School, San Jose)*

Colorado
Janeane Golliher *(St. Vrain Valley School District, Longmont)*; Judith Koenig *(Nevin Platt Middle School, Boulder)*

Florida
Paige Loggins *(Swift Creek Middle School, Tallahassee)*

Illinois
Jan Robinson *(School District #21, Wheeling)*

Indiana
Frances Jackson *(Joseph L. Block Junior High, East Chicago)*

Kentucky
Natalee Feese *(Fayette County Public Schools, Lexington)*

Maine
Betsy Berry *(Maine Math & Science Alliance, Augusta)*

Maryland
Joseph Gagnon *(University of Maryland, College Park)*; Paula Maccini *(University of Maryland, College Park)*

Massachusetts
George Cobb *(Mt. Holyoke College, South Hadley)*; Cliff Kanold *(University of Massachusetts, Amherst)*

Michigan
Mary Bouck *(Farwell Area Schools)*; Carol Dorer *(Slauson Middle School, Ann Arbor)*; Carrie Heaney *(Forsythe Middle School, Ann Arbor)*; Ellen Hopkins *(Clague Middle School, Ann Arbor)*; Teri Keusch *(Portland Middle School, Portland)*; Valerie Mills *(Oakland Schools, Waterford)*; Mary Beth Schmitt *(Traverse City East Junior High, Traverse City)*; Jack Smith *(Michigan State University, East Lansing)*; Rebecca Spencer *(Sparta Middle School, Sparta)*; Ann Marie Nicoll Turner *(Tappan Middle School, Ann Arbor)*; Scott Turner *(Scarlett Middle School, Ann Arbor)*

Minnesota
Margarita Alvarez *(Olson Middle School, Minneapolis)*; Jane Amundson *(Nicollet Junior High, Burnsville)*; Anne Bartel *(Minneapolis Public Schools)*; Gwen Ranzau Campbell *(Sunrise Park Middle School, White Bear Lake)*; Stephanie Cin *(Hidden Valley Elementary, Burnsville)*; Joan Garfield *(University of Minnesota, Minneapolis)*; Gretchen Hall *(Richfield Middle School, Richfield)*; Jennifer Larson *(Olson Middle School, Minneapolis)*; Michele Luke *(West Junior High, Minnetonka)*; Jeni Meyer *(Richfield Junior High, Richfield)*; Judy Pfingsten *(Inver Grove Heights Middle School, Inver Grove Heights)*; Sarah Shafer *(North Junior High, Minnetonka)*; Genni Steele *(Central Middle School, White Bear Lake)*; Victoria Wilson *(Eisenhower Elementary, Hopkins)*; Paul Zorn *(St. Olaf College, Northfield)*

New York
Debra Altenau-Bartolino *(Greenwich Village Middle School, New York)*; Doug Clements *(University of Buffalo)*; Francis Curcio *(New York University, New York)*; Christine Dorosh *(Clinton School for Writers, Brooklyn)*; Jennifer Rehn *(East Side Middle School, New York)*; Phyllis Tam *(IS 89 Lab School, New York)*;

Marie Turini *(Louis Armstrong Middle School, New York)*; Lucy West *(Community School District 2, New York)*; Monica Witt *(Simon Baruch Intermediate School 104, New York)*

Pennsylvania
Robert Aglietti *(Pittsburgh)*; Sharon Mihalich *(Freeport)*; Jennifer Plumb *(South Hills Middle School, Pittsburgh)*; Mary Lynn Raith *(Pittsburgh Public Schools)*

Texas
Michelle Bittick *(Austin Independent School District)*; Margaret Cregg *(Plano Independent School District)*; Sheila Cunningham *(Klein Independent School District)*; Judy Hill *(Austin Independent School District)*; Patricia Holguin *(El Paso Independent School District)*; Bonnie McNemar *(Arlington)*; Kay Neuse *(Plano Independent School District)*; Joyce Polanco *(Austin Independent School District)*; Marge Ramirez *(University of Texas at El Paso)*; Pat Rossman *(Baker Campus, Austin)*; Cindy Schimek *(Houston)*; Cynthia Schneider *(Charles A. Dana Center, University of Texas at Austin)*; Uri Treisman *(Charles A. Dana Center, University of Texas at Austin)*; Jacqueline Weilmuenster *(Grapevine-Colleyville Independent School District)*; LuAnn Weynand *(San Antonio)*; Carmen Whitman *(Austin Independent School District)*; James Wohlgehagen *(Plano Independent School District)*

Washington
Ramesh Gangolli *(University of Washington, Seattle)*

Wisconsin
Susan Lamon *(Marquette University, Hales Corner)*; Steve Reinhart *(retired, Chippewa Falls Middle School, Eau Claire)*

Accentuate the Negative
Integers and Rational Numbers

> The Student Edition pages for the Unit Opener follow page 12.

Accentuate the Negative
Integers and Rational Numbers

Goals of the Unit

- Use appropriate notation to indicate positive and negative numbers

- Locate rational numbers (positive and negative fractions and decimals and zero) on a number line

- Compare and order rational numbers

- Understand the relationship between a positive or negative number and its opposite (additive inverse)

- Develop algorithms for adding, subtracting, multiplying, and dividing positive and negative numbers

- Write mathematics sentences to show relationships

- Write and use related fact families for addition/subtraction and multiplication/division to solve simple equations with missing facts

- Use parentheses and order of operations to make computational sequences clear

- Understand and use the Commutative Property for addition and multiplication of positive and negative numbers

- Apply the Distributive Property with positive and negative numbers to simplify expressions and solve problems

- Use positive and negative numbers to graph in four quadrants and to model and answer questions about applied settings

Developing Students' Mathematical Habits

The overall goal of *Connected Mathematics* is to help students develop sound mathematical habits. Through their work in this number unit, students learn important questions to ask themselves about any situation that can be represented and modeled mathematically, such as:

- *How do negative and positive numbers help in describing the situation?*

- *What will addition, subtraction, multiplication, or division of positive and negative numbers tell about the problem?*

- *What model(s) for positive and negative numbers would help in showing the relationships in the problem situation?*

Overview

In the middle grades, students are introduced to fractions and decimals. The next major hurdle is building an understanding of positive and negative numbers, i.e., integers, fractions, and decimals. Students have experienced these kinds of numbers informally in their everyday world. For example, temperatures drop below zero in the winter or soar above 90 degrees in the summer, and sports teams are said to be ahead or behind by so much. Students have intuitively used operations on integers to make sense of these situations. This unit explores situations that require representation with positive and negative numbers. These situations motivate more formal ways to add, subtract, multiply, and divide these numbers. Students formalize algorithms for operating using positive and negative numbers. They also consider the order of operations and selected properties.

Summary of Investigations

Investigation 1

Extending the Number System

This investigation gives students experiences with positive and negative numbers, ordering, and informal operations in a variety of contexts so that subsequent formal work can be based on "what makes sense." Positive and negative numbers in the form of integers, fractions, and decimals are also represented on a number line.

Investigation 2

Adding and Subtracting Integers

Students build on the informal work of Investigation 1 to formulate algorithms for addition and subtraction of positive and negative numbers. In each problem, students are encouraged to think about the meaning of the operations from several perspectives and use different representation models (number line and chip board).

Investigation 3

Multiplying and Dividing Integers

This investigation is structured and developed in a style parallel to that of Investigation 2. The number line model and fact families as well as the contexts of time, distance, and speed are used to develop students' understanding of multiplication and division of positive and negative numbers. Since students have not done much informal multiplication and division, a useful context for questions leading to multiplication and division is explained before asking students to formulate algorithms. The context involves motion at various rates in both directions on a number line. The cases of a negative number times a positive number and a negative number divided by a positive number could come quite easily from the chip board context. However, that model doesn't seem to lead naturally to those cases that involve the product or quotient of two negatives. In almost any context, you have to think hard to get a reasonable guide to the operations we want to develop. In the time, rate, distance, and position setting, these ideas are plausible. The cases of combinations of "signs" for multiplication are explained by looking at number patterns.

Investigation 4

Properties of Operations

Students compare algebraic properties of the operations on positive and negative numbers (i.e. the rational numbers) to those of the number system of only positive numbers (whole numbers). It's not intended to be a full-scale treatment of field properties of the real numbers.

Mathematics Background

Most students may be able to add, subtract, multiply, and divide whole numbers, fractions, and decimals. However, most have not been asked to think about what the operations mean and what kinds of situations call for which operation. Students need the development of the disposition to seek ways of making sense of mathematical ideas and skills. Otherwise, they may end up with technical skills but without ways of deciding when and how those skills can be used to solve problems.

One way to develop the desire to make sense of these ideas is to model such thinking in classroom conversation. Asking questions about meaning, (about what makes sense) as a regular, expected part of classroom discourse helps focus students on making connections. Exploring new aspects of numbers in a way that builds on and connects to what they already know is likely to have two good effects. First, students will deepen their understanding of familiar numbers and operations. Second, the new numbers, integers, and negative rational numbers will be more deeply integrated into students' own mathematical knowledge and resources.

Students find several things difficult about working with positive and negative numbers.

- The fact that -27 is less than -12 is contrary to students' experience with whole numbers (positive integers and zero). This understanding requires building mental images and models that allow students to visualize these new comparisons and relationships.

- The operation of subtraction, especially of subtracting a negative number, is difficult for students to understand. In this unit, students will have several opportunities to think about what makes sense and why. They will encounter representations and models that will help them better understand subtraction.

- The idea that subtracting a negative number gives the same result as adding the opposite of the negative number (adding a positive) is difficult for many students. This understanding must develop over time as students make observations and comparisons between subtraction and addition. Recognizing that these are inverse operations and that addition sentences are related to subtraction sentences helps students to expand their understanding of this concept.

- Multiplying two negatives and getting a positive number does not make sense to many students. In fact, the usual ways of giving meaning to multiplication, such as repeatedly adding an amount, seem of little help in making sense of $-12 \times (-5)$.

- In the unit, we approach these difficult concepts of subtracting a negative and multiplying two negatives through the use of set and number line models and the relationships that exist between addition and subtraction and multiplication and division.

- A number of other confusions occur. For example, the idea that a negative rational number names a point on the number line or knowing that $-3\frac{1}{2}$ can be thought of as $-3 + (-\frac{1}{2})$ is often not transparent.

Using Models for Integers and the Operations of Addition and Subtraction

The number line is a model that is used throughout the number units. It was first introduced in *Bits and Pieces I* to develop understanding of equivalence of fractions and decimals. It was used in *Bits and Pieces II and III* to help develop the operations for fractions and decimals. It is used later in *Looking for Pythagoras* to introduce square roots and irrational numbers. In this unit, students use the directed distance model with the number line to visualize adding and subtracting integers. Here are two situations that students encounter that use both *distance* and *direction* as ways to consider integers.

> *The world record for fastest rise in outside air temperature occurred in Spearfish, South Dakota, on January 22, 1943. The temperature rose from $^-4°F$ to $^+45°F$ in two minutes. What was the change in temperature over those two minutes?*

On a number line, this change can be shown using an arrow. (Figure 1)

A student might reason: "From $^-4°F$ to $0°F$ is an increase of $^+4°F$, and from $0°F$ to $45°F$ is an increase of $^+45°F$. So the total change is an increase of $^+49°F$." The situation can be described with a number sentence:

$$^-4° + n = {}^+45° \quad \text{or} \quad {}^-4° + {}^+49° = {}^+45°$$

The sign of the change in temperature shows the direction of the change. If the temperature had dropped $10°F$, the student would write the change as $^-10°F$ to show the size and direction of the change. (Figure 2)

$$^-4° + n = {}^-14° \quad \text{or} \quad {}^-4° + {}^-10° = {}^-14°$$

Figure 1

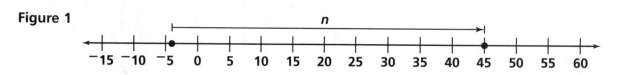

We can write these equations without the degree markers. We just have to remember what the answer means. To facilitate the development of the algorithms, the absolute value concept is introduced in Investigation 2 as a way to talk about distance on the number line. It also helps to talk about the value of a number when direction is not considered.

Colored chips can also be used to develop a strategy for adding and subtracting integers. Using this model requires an understanding of opposites. For example, $^-3$ and $^+3$ are opposite because $^+3 + {}^-3 = 0$, or each number is equidistant from the origin on the number line. Red-black pairs represent opposites ($^-1$ and $^+1$), which add to 0. The chip model uses one color of chips (black) to represent positive integers and another color (red) to represent negative integers. (**Note:** You may use any collection of two-color chips—designate which color is positive and which color is negative.)

To use the model with addition, begin with an empty chip board. Place chips on the board to represent each addend. If the integer is positive, place that number of black chips on the board. If the integer is negative, place that number of red chips on the board. If the two integers being added have the same sign, the sum is the total number of chips on the board. For example, to add $^-4 + {}^-3$, place 4 red chips and then another 3 red chips on the board for a total of 7 red chips (representing a sum of $^-7$, or $^-4 + {}^-3 = {}^-7$).

If the integers being added have different signs, place the appropriate number of red and black chips on the board to represent each addend. Simplify the board by removing red-black (opposite) pairs of chips. The chips that remain unmatched represent the sum of the two integers. Consider this problem:

> *Linda owes her sister $6 for helping her cut the lawn. She earns $4 delivering papers with her brother. Is she "in the red" or "in the black"?*

Using collections of black and red chips on a chip board, you can represent the combination of expense and income.

Chip Board

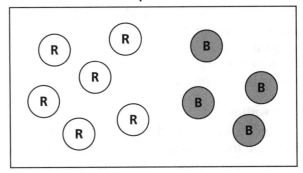

The result, or net worth, is that Linda is "in the red" 2 dollars, or $^-2$ dollars. This problem may be represented with the number sentence, $^-6 + {}^+4 = {}^-2$.

Because each chip represents 1 unit, either positive or negative, red and black chips are thought of as opposites. Combining two opposite chips makes zero ($^+1 + {}^-1 = 0$). In this problem, we can rewrite $^-6$ as $^-2 + {}^-4$ so that 4 chips of each color can be paired to make zeros ($^-6 + {}^+4 = {}^-2 + {}^-4 + {}^+4 = {}^-2 + 0$). After the paired chips are removed, 2 red chips remain. These chips represent the sum $^-2$ ($^-2 + 0 = {}^-2$).

Here is another problem that can be modeled and solved using chips:

> *Jeremy earns $10 mowing a lawn. He needs to pay $15 to rent his equipment. How much more money does he need to pay the rental cost?*

This problem may be modeled using chips by representing the $10 with a combination of 15 black and 5 red chips ($10 = {}^-5 + 15$). Now $15 or 15 black chips can be "taken away" [$^-5 + (15 - 15)$], leaving 5 red chips to represent the $^-5$ that Jeremy is "short." Two different number sentences are applicable:

$^+10 + {}^-15 = {}^-5$ and $^+10 - {}^+15 = {}^-5$

As students work on adding and subtracting integers, they notice that it may be helpful to restate an addition problem as a subtraction

Figure 2

$^-10$

$^-15$ $^-10$ $^-5$ 0 5 10 15 20 25 30 35 40 45 50 55 60

problem or vice versa. This involves using opposites of numbers. For example:

To calculate $^+12 + ^-8$, they may realize that the result is the same as when they subtract $^+8$ in the problem $^+12 - ^+8$.

For $^+5 - ^-7$, they may realize that the result is the same as when they add $^+7$ in $^+5 + ^+7$.

Students build on generalizations made using models of integers to extend their work with negative and positive rational numbers.

Fact Families

Fact families are used in this unit to help students understand the relationship between addition and subtraction and between multiplication and division. Fact families were introduced in the number units in grade 6. Here is an example of a fact family:

$$^-7 + ^+2 = ^-5 \qquad ^-5 - ^+2 = ^-7$$
$$^+2 + ^-7 = ^-5 \qquad ^-5 - ^-7 = ^+2$$

Fact families are also used to find a missing factor or addend such as:

$$^+4 + n = ^+43 \text{ or } ^-6n = 42$$

Models and the Operations of Multiplication and Division

Multiplication can be explored using a number line model and "counting" occurrences of fixed-size movement along the number line. Direction of movement introduces negative and positive movements. For example:

Hahn passes the 0 point running 5 meters per second to the right. Where is he 10 seconds later?

Aurelia passes the 0 point running to the left at 6 meters per second. Where is she 8 seconds later?

Relating division to multiplication helps develop division with integers. A multiplication fact can be used as the basis for creating two related division facts. By developing division this way, students can determine the sign of the answer to a division problem. For example, since we know that $5 \times (^-2) = ^-10$ (or $^-2 \times 5 = ^-10$), we can write related division sentences:

$$^-10 \div (^-2) = 5 \quad \text{and} \quad ^-10 \div 5 = ^-2$$

Then, students can generalize rules for handling the sign of the quotient in a division problem.

Some Notes on Notation

Writing integers with raised signs avoids confusion with symbols for addition and subtraction. However, most software and most writing in mathematics do not use the raised signs.

Positive numbers are usually written without a sign.

$$^+3 = 3 \text{ and } ^+7.5 = 7.5.$$

Negative numbers are usually written with a dash like a subtraction sign.

$$^-3 = ^-3 \text{ and } ^-7.5 = ^-7.5.$$

Parentheses can help.

$$^-5 - ^-8 = ^-5 - ^-8 = ^-5 - (^-8)$$

The subtraction symbol also indicates the opposite of a number. For example, $^-8$ represents the opposite of 8 and $^-(^-8)$ the opposite of $^-8$.

$$^-(^-8) = 8$$

We use raised signs for the first two investigations, after which we use the standard notation.

For multiplication, you can use a raised dot symbol. For example, $3 \times 5 = 3 \cdot 5$. Some students might have seen $3 \cdot (4 + 5)$ or $3 \times (4 + 5)$, or even $3(4 + 5)$.

Order of Operations and Properties

Order of operations rules are introduced.

1. Compute any expressions within parentheses.
   $$(^-7 - 2) + 1 = ^-9 + 1 = ^-8$$
   $$(1 + 2) \times (-4) = 3 \times (^-4) = ^-12$$

2. Compute any exponents.
   $$^-2 + 3^2 = ^-2 + 9 = 7$$
   $$6 - (^-1 + 4)^2 = 6 - (3)^2 = ^-3$$

3. Multiply and divide in order, from left to right.
   Example 1
   $$\begin{array}{ll} 1 + 2 \times 4 = & \text{Multiplication first} \\ 1 + 8 = \ 9 & \end{array}$$
   Example 2
   $$\begin{array}{ll} 200 \div 10 \times 2 = & \text{Division first} \\ 20 \times 2 = \ 40 & \text{Multiplication second} \end{array}$$

4. Add and subtract in order, from left to right.
   $$\begin{array}{ll} 1 - 2 + 3 \times 4 = & \text{Multiplication first} \\ 1 - 2 + 12 = & \text{Addition and} \\ & \text{subtraction} \\ ^-1 + 12 = \ 11 & \end{array}$$

The Commutative Property of Addition and Multiplication is introduced. Students find that this property does not hold for subtraction or division of integers. The Distributive Property of Multiplication over Addition or Subtraction is also introduced and modeled through finding areas of rectangles. The Associative Property is explored in an ACE exercise. These properties are revisited in several succeeding units, particularly the algebra units.

Big Idea	Prior Work	Future Work
Defining and developing understanding of positive and negative numbers	Developing understanding of whole numbers and rational numbers (*Prime Time, Bits and Pieces I, II, & III*)	Interpreting and applying positive and negative slopes of lines and positive and negative coefficients in equations (*Moving Straight Ahead, Thinking With Mathematical Models, Say It With Symbols, The Shapes of Algebra*); developing understanding of square roots and irrational numbers (*Looking for Pythagoras*)
Exploring relationships between positive and negative numbers (e.g., interpreting positive numbers as a loss and negative numbers as a gain)	Using models to develop understanding of mathematical concepts (*Bits and Pieces I, II, & III, Covering and Surrounding, Ruins of Montarek, Stretching and Shrinking, Comparing and Scaling*)	Understanding relationships between positive and negative coefficients or values for variables (*Moving Straight Ahead, Thinking With Mathematical Models, Say It With Symbols, The Shapes of Algebra*); using positive and negative integers to communicate directions in two dimensions (*Kaleidoscopes, Hubcaps, and Mirrors*)
Developing understanding of arithmetic operations with positive and negative numbers	Understanding and applying arithmetic operations with rational numbers (*Bits and Pieces II & III, Stretching and Shrinking, Comparing and Scaling*)	Evaluating algebraic expressions involving positive and negative coefficients or values for variables (*Moving Straight Ahead, Data Distributions, Thinking With Mathematical Models; Frogs, Fleas, and Painted Cubes; Say It With Symbols, The Shapes of Algebra, Clever Counting* ©2004); interpreting isometries in the plane given in symbolic form (*Kaleidoscopes, Hubcaps, and Mirrors*)
Extending the number line and coordinate grid to include negative coordinates	Using a coordinate grid with positive coordinates (*Data About Us, Covering and Surrounding, Variables and Patterns, Stretching and Shrinking*); using a number line to develop equivalence and operations of fractions and decimals (*Bits I, II, and III*)	Graphing equations on coordinate grids (*Moving Straight Ahead, Data Distributions, Thinking With Mathematical Models; Growing, Growing, Growing; Frogs, Fleas, and Painted Cubes; Say It With Symbols, The Shapes of Algebra; Kaleidoscopes, Hubcaps, and Mirrors*); locating square roots on the number line (*Looking for Pythagoras*)
Developing understanding of the Commutative Property, the Distributive Property, and the order of operations	Developing understanding of the Commutative Property using whole numbers and rational numbers (*Prime Time, Bits and Pieces II & III*); using the order of operations to solve problems in a context (*Covering and Surrounding, Variables and Patterns*)	Using the properties and order of operations to write equivalent expressions and solve equations (*Moving Straight Ahead, Thinking With Mathematical Models; Growing, Growing, Growing; Frogs, Fleas, and Painted Cubes; Say It With Symbols, The Shapes of Algebra*)

Planning for the Unit

Pacing Suggestions and Materials

Investigations and Assessments	Pacing 45–50 min. classes	Materials for Students	Materials for Teachers
1 Extending the Number System	$4\frac{1}{2}$ days	Chips or tiles in two colors, Labsheet 1ACE Exercises 31 and 48, Number Lines, Chip Board, and Small Chip Boards labsheets	Chips or tiles in two colors, Transparencies 1.1A, 1.1B, 1.2, 1.3, 1.4A, 1.4B, Number Lines, Thermometer, and Chip Boards transparencies
Mathematical Reflections	$\frac{1}{2}$ day		
2 Adding and Subtracting Integers	$5\frac{1}{2}$ days	Chips or tiles in two colors, rulers or straightedges, Labsheets 2.5, Number Lines and Coordinate Grid labsheets	Chips or tiles in two colors, Transparencies 2.1A, 2.1B, 2.2A, 2.2B, 2.2C, 2.3, 2.5, Number Lines, Coordinate Grid, and Chip Boards transparencies
Mathematical Reflections	$\frac{1}{2}$ day		
Assessment: Partner Quiz	1 day		
3 Multiplying and Dividing Integers	4 days	Paper clips (2 per pair), colored pens, markers, or pencils, Labsheets 3.4, 3ACE Exercise 25 parts (a) and (b), 3ACE Exercise 25 parts (c) and (d), Number Lines labsheet	2 paper clips, Transparencies 3.1A, 3.1B, 3.2, 3.3A, 3.3B, 3.4, Number Lines transparency
Mathematical Reflections	$\frac{1}{2}$ day		
Assessment: Check Up	$\frac{1}{2}$ day		
4 Properties of Operations	4 days		Transparencies 4.1A, 4.1B, 4.2A, 4.2B, 4.3
Mathematical Reflections	$\frac{1}{2}$ day		
Looking Back and Looking Ahead	1 day		
Assessment: Unit Project	optional	Labsheets UP.A, UP.B	
Assessment: Self Assessment	Take Home		
Assessment: Unit Test	1 day		

Total Time $23\frac{1}{2}$ days	Materials for Use in All Investigations	
For detailed pacing for Problems within each Investigation, see the Suggested Pacing at the beginning of each Investigation.	Calculators, blank transparencies and transparency markers (optional), student notebooks	Blank transparencies and transparency markers (optional)
For pacing with block scheduling, see next page.		

Pacing for Block Scheduling (90-minute class periods)

Investigation	Suggested Pacing	Investigation	Suggested Pacing
Investigation 1	**3 days**	**Investigation 3**	$2\frac{1}{2}$ **days**
Problem 1.1	1 day	Problem 3.1	$\frac{1}{2}$ day
Problem 1.2	$\frac{1}{2}$ day	Problem 3.2	$\frac{1}{2}$ day
Problem 1.3	$\frac{1}{2}$ day	Problem 3.3	$\frac{1}{2}$ day
Problem 1.4	$\frac{1}{2}$ day	Problem 3.4	$\frac{1}{2}$ day
Math Reflections	$\frac{1}{2}$ day	Math Reflections	$\frac{1}{2}$ day
Investigation 2	$3\frac{1}{2}$ **days**	**Investigation 4**	**3 days**
Problem 2.1	$\frac{1}{2}$ day	Problem 4.1	$\frac{1}{2}$ day
Problem 2.2	1 day	Problem 4.2	1 day
Problem 2.3	$\frac{1}{2}$ day	Problem 4.3	$\frac{1}{2}$ day
Problem 2.4	$\frac{1}{2}$ day	Math Reflections	$\frac{1}{2}$ day
Problem 2.5	$\frac{1}{2}$ day		
Math Reflections	$\frac{1}{2}$ day		

Vocabulary

Essential Terms Developed in This Unit	Useful Terms Referenced in This Unit	Terms Developed in Previous Units
Commutative Property	absolute value	algorithm*
Distributive Property	additive inverse	area*
integers	Associative Property	coordinate grid
negative numbers	expanding	decimals*
opposites	factoring	expression
order of operations	quadrant I, II, III, and IV	fact family*
positive numbers		fractions*
rational numbers		income/profit
		mathematical sentence*
		number line*
		number sentence*
		operations*
		ordered pair
		variable

*developed in previous year

Components

Use the chart below to quickly see which components are available for each Investigation.

Invest.	Labsheets	Additional Practice	Transparencies		Formal Assessment		Assessment Options	
			Problem	Summary	Check Up	Partner Quiz	Multiple-Choice	Question Bank
1	1ACE Exercises 31 and 48	✔	1.1A, 1.1B, 1.2, 1.3, 1.4A, 1.4B				✔	✔
2	2.5	✔	2.1A, 2.1B, 2.2A–C, 2.3, 2.5			✔	✔	✔
3	3.4, 3ACE Exercise 25 parts (a) and (b), 3ACE Exercise 25 parts (c) and (d)	✔	3.1A, 3.1B, 3.2, 3.3A, 3.3B, 3.4		✔		✔	✔
4		✔	4.1A, 4.1B, 4.2A, 4.2B, 4.3				✔	✔
Project	UP.A, UP.B							
For the Unit	Score Sheet and Cards for Dealing Down, Number Lines, Chip Boards, Coordinate Grid, Graph Paper	*ExamView* CD-ROM, Web site	LBLA		Unit Test, Unit Project Notebook Check, Self Assessment		Multiple-Choice, Question Bank, *ExamView* CD-ROM	

Also Available for Use With This Unit

- Parent Guide: take-home letter for the unit
- Implementing CMP
- Spanish Assessment Resources
- Additional online and technology resources

Technology

The Use of Calculators

Most of the numbers in this unit are kept reasonably small so that students can focus on signed numbers and their arithmetic. Calculators can be used in places to explore patterns and confirm computations.

Student Activity CD-ROM

Includes interactive activities to enhance the learning in the Problems within Investigations.

PHSchool.com

For Students Multiple-choice practice with instant feedback, updated data sources, and data sets for Tinkerplots software.

For Teachers Professional development, curriculum support, downloadable forms, and more.

See also www.math.msu.edu/cmp for more resources for both teachers and students.

ExamView® CD-ROM

Create multiple versions of practice sheets and tests for course objectives and standardized tests. Includes dynamic questions, online testing, student reports, and all test and practice items in Spanish. Also includes all items in the *Assessment Resources* and *Additional Practice*.

Teacher Express™ CD-ROM

Includes a lesson planning tool, the Teacher's Guide pages, and all the teaching resources.

LessonLab Online Courses

LessonLab offers comprehensive, facilitated professional development designed to help teachers implement CMP2 and improve student achievement. To learn more, please visit PHSchool.com/cmp2.

Ongoing Informal Assessment

Embedded in the Student Unit

Problems Use students' work from the Problems to check student understanding.

ACE exercises Use ACE exercises for homework assignments to assess student understanding.

Mathematical Reflections Have students summarize their learning at the end of each Investigation.

Looking Back and Looking Ahead At the end of the unit, use the first two sections to allow students to show what they know about the unit.

Additional Resources

Teacher's Guide Use the Check for Understanding feature of some Summaries and the probing questions that appear in the *Launch, Explore,* or *Summarize* sections of all Investigations to check student understanding.

Self Assessment

Notebook Check Students use this tool to organize and check their notebooks before giving them to their teacher. Located in *Assessment Resources.*

Self Assessment At the end of the unit, students reflect on and provide examples of what they learned. Located in *Assessment Resources.*

Formal Assessment

Choose the assessment materials that are appropriate for your students.

Assessment	For Use After	Focus	Student Work
Partner Quiz	Invest. 2	Rich problems	Pair
Check Up	Invest. 3	Skills	Individual
Unit Test	The Unit	Skills, rich problems	Individual
Unit Project	The Unit	Rich problems	Individual or Group

Additional Resources

Multiple-Choice Items Use these items for homework, review, a quiz, or add them to the Unit Test.

Question Bank Choose from these questions for homework, review, or replacements for Quiz, Check Up, or Unit Test questions.

Additional Practice Choose practice exercises for each investigation for homework, review, or formal assessments.

***ExamView* CD-ROM** Create practice sheets, review quizzes, and tests with this dynamic software. Give online tests and receive student progress reports. (All test items are also available in Spanish.)

Spanish Assessment Resources

Includes Partner Quizzes, Check Ups, Unit Test, Multiple-Choice Items, Question Bank, Notebook Check, and Self Assessment. Plus, the *ExamView* CD-ROM has all test items in Spanish.

Correlation to Standardized Tests

Investigation	NAEP	Terra Nova				Local Test
		CAT6	CTBS	ITBS	SAT10	
1 Extending the Number System	N1b, N1i, N1j, N3g	✔	✔	✔	✔	
2 Adding and Subtracting Integers	N1g, N3a, N3f, N3g, N5e	✔	✔	✔		
3 Multiplying and Dividing Integers	N3a, N3d, N3f, N3g, N5e	✔	✔	✔		
4 Properties of Operations	N3a, N3f, N3g, N5e	✔	✔	✔	✔	

NAEP National Assessment of Educational Progress

CAT6/Terra Nova California Achievement Test, 6th Ed.
CTBS/Terra Nova Comprehensive Test of Basic Skills

ITBS Iowa Test of Basic Skills, Form M
SAT10 Stanford Achievement Test, 10th Ed.

Introducing Your Students to *Accentuate the Negative*

This unit is about extending the kinds of numbers that we use and on which we operate. Remind students that in early elementary grades, their number system only included the whole numbers. Then they learned about fractions and decimal fractions. Now they are going to extend the set of numbers to include new numbers that help them model situations and solve new kinds of problems.

Using the Unit Opener

Helping students see how the unit connects with their interests and builds on what they already may know helps them to learn new content. It supports the integration of this knowledge through application.

Read through the introductory page and discuss the three problems with your students. The problems will be answered within the unit, so students are not expected to be able to solve them here. The problems serve as a preview of what the students will encounter and learn during the unit. Allow your students to share their ideas with the goal of generating enthusiasm for the kinds of situations they will encounter in the unit.

Talk with the class about what they know about negative and positive numbers as they are encountered in everyday conversations. Keep the conversations focused on eliciting what students think rather than on trying to define the topic mathematically. When students propose situations in which they think negative and positive numbers are used, ask them to explain how they are used.

You can use the Table of Contents to help students anticipate what is in the unit and to build a set of expectations for the work they will do.

Using the Mathematical Highlights

The Mathematical Highlights page in the Student Edition provides information to students, parents, and other family members. It gives students a preview of the mathematics and some of the overarching questions that they should ask themselves while studying *Accentuate the Negative*.

As they work through the unit, students can refer back to the Mathematical Highlights page to review what they have learned and to preview what is still to come. This page also tells students' families what mathematical ideas and activities will be covered as the class works through *Accentuate the Negative*.

Problems in contexts are used to help students informally reason about the mathematics of the unit. The problems are deliberately sequenced to develop understanding of concepts and skills.

Using the Unit Project

The optional unit project, *Dealing Down*, allows students to apply what they have learned about operating with integers, using the Distributive and Commutative properties, and applying the order of operations to make computational sequences clear.

The project has two parts. First, students play a game where they find the least quantity using four number cards drawn from a set. After playing a few rounds of the game, students write a report explaining their strategies for the game and their use of the mathematics of the unit to write an expression for the least possible quantity.

To play the game, students will need one set of number cards for each group of 3–4 students. Students can record the results of the game on the Dealing Down Score Sheet or in a table like the one in the Student Edition. A time limit for each round will keep the game progressing at a reasonable speed. The game can be played during one class period. The report can be assigned as an individual assignment done outside of class.

A scoring rubric and samples of student work are given on pages 104–108 in the Guide to the Unit Project.

Connected Mathematics 2

Accentuate the Negative

Integers and Rational Numbers

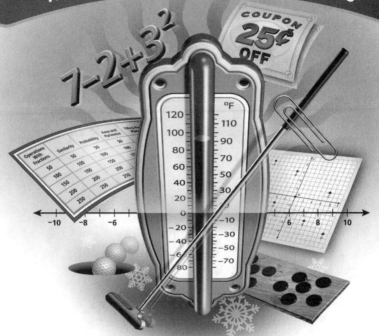

Glenda Lappan
James T. Fey
William M. Fitzgerald
Susan N. Friel
Elizabeth Difanis Phillips

PEARSON

Boston, Massachusetts · Glenview, Illinois · Shoreview, Minnesota · Upper Saddle River, New Jersey

Notes _____

_____

_____

_____

Accentuate the Negative

After the first five questions in a quiz show, player A has a score of −100 and player B has a score of −150. Which player has the lead and how great is the lead?

Hahn competes in a relay race. He goes from the 0 meter line to the 15 meter line in 5 seconds. At what rate (distance per second) does he run?

A new convenience store wants to attract customers. For a one-day special, they sell gasoline for $0.25 below their cost. They sell 5,750 gallons that day. How much money do they lose?

2   Accentuate the Negative

Notes _____

_____

_____

_____

Most of the numbers you have worked with in math class this year have been greater than or equal to zero. However, numbers less than zero can provide important information. Winter temperatures in many places fall below 0°F. Businesses that lose money have profits less than $0. Scores in games or sports can be less than zero.

Numbers greater than zero are called *positive numbers.* Numbers less than zero are called *negative numbers.* In *Accentuate the Negative,* you will work with both positive and negative numbers. One subset of positive and negative numbers that you will study is called *integers.* You will explore models that help you think about adding, subtracting, multiplying, and dividing positive and negative numbers. You will also learn more about the properties of operations on positive and negative numbers.

In *Accentuate the Negative,* you will solve problems similar to those on the previous page that require understanding and skill in working with positive and negative numbers.

STUDENT PAGE

Notes _____

_____

_____

_____

In *Accentuate the Negative*, you will extend your knowledge of negative numbers. You will explore ways to use negative numbers in solving problems.

You will learn how to

- Use appropriate notation to indicate positive and negative numbers
- Compare and order positive and negative rational numbers (fractions, decimals, and zero) and locate them on a number line
- Understand the relationship between a positive or negative number and its opposite (additive inverse)
- Develop algorithms for adding, subtracting, multiplying, and dividing positive and negative numbers
- Write mathematical sentences to show relationships
- Write and use related fact families for addition/subtraction and multiplication/division to solve simple equations
- Use parentheses and rules for the order of operations in computations
- Understand and use the Commutative Property for addition and multiplication
- Apply the Distributive Property to simplify expressions and solve problems
- Graph points in four quadrants
- Use positive and negative numbers to model and answer questions about problem situations

As you work on problems in this unit, ask yourself questions like these:

How do negative and positive numbers help in describing the situation?

What will addition, subtraction, multiplication, or division of positive and negative numbers tell about the problem?

What model(s) for positive and negative numbers would help in showing the relationships in the problem situation?

Notes _____

_____

_____

_____

Mathematical and Problem-Solving Goals

- Explore the use of and appropriate notation for positive and negative numbers in applied settings
- Interpret and write mathematical sentences
- Locate positive and negative numbers on a number line and compare and order them
- Understand the relationship between a positive or negative number and its opposite (additive inverse)
- Write number sentences to reflect the actions and results of changes in situations and find missing values
- Develop and use both a number line and a chip model for representing addition and subtraction

Summary of Problems

Problem 1.1 Playing Math Fever

This problem builds on students' intuitions about negative numbers with money and asks questions that may be represented by addition or related subtraction operations. This is a good opportunity for teachers to learn what their students already know about integers and ways of operating on them. Teachers do not need to show students standard algorithms for adding or subtracting signed numbers at this time. Informal arithmetic reasoning will help students solve most of the problems.

Problem 1.2 From Sauna to Snowbank

This problem uses temperature measurement and change via thermometers to extend a number line to include negative numbers. Students develop informal strategies for ordering and locating a number and its opposite on a number line, recognizing that both absolute value and direction matter.

	Suggested Pacing	Materials for Students	Materials for Teachers	ACE Assignments
All	5 days	Student notebooks	Blank transparencies and transparency markers	
1.1	$1\frac{1}{2}$ days	Labsheet 1ACE Exercises 31 and 48	Transparencies 1.1A, 1.1B	1–8, 39, 48
1.2	1 day	Number Lines labsheet	Transparency 1.2, Number Lines or Thermometers transparency	9–19, 40, 41, 44–47, 49–51
1.3	1 day	Labsheet 1ACE Exercises 31 and 48, Number Lines labsheet	Transparency 1.3, Number Lines transparency	20–31, 42, 43
1.4	1 day	Chips or tiles in two colors (about 15–25 of each per pair of students; Student Edition refers to red and black), Chip Board and Small Chip Boards labsheets (optional)	Transparencies 1.4A, 1.4B, Chip Boards transparency (optional), chips or tiles in two colors	32–38, 52–54
MR	$\frac{1}{2}$ day			

Problem 1.3 What's the Change?

Students write numbers and sketch number lines to show changing temperatures and the resulting temperature. Once again, students are not expected to solve these problems by following some specific algorithm for signed numbers. They should use informal arithmetic reasoning to connect direction and distance to the number line and represent their reasoning with number sentences.

Problem 1.4 In the Chips

Students connect the operations of addition and subtraction (including the relationships between these two operations) to actions on chip board displays. Black chips indicate positive values, and red chips indicate negative values. This model lends itself to the "take away" interpretation of subtraction.

1.1 Playing Math Fever

Goals

- Explore the use of and appropriate notation for positive and negative numbers in applied settings

- Interpret and write mathematical sentences

Math Fever is an easy and engaging way to begin students' work with signed numbers. You can introduce the context by asking students to describe game shows like *Jeopardy!*®. Make sure the class discusses how points are earned. When a contestant answers a question correctly, he or she receives the points (money) assigned to that question. When a contestant misses a question, the points for that question are deducted from his or her score.

On page 19, you will find some sample questions for Math Fever in case you have time to play the game with your students.

Launch 1.1

Explore extending the number line. Display a number line that can be copied by each student to place the numbers as shown. Have students label the integer points from ⁻10 to 10 on the number line. Then locate some fractional and decimal fraction values between the integers. Use the diagram of opposites and have students draw such connectors between some of the number pairs to show opposites on their number lines. Use the Getting Ready to segue into Problem 1.1.

Discuss the introduction to the Math Fever game with your students. Put the scores of the three teams (Super Brains, Rocket Scientists, and Know-It-Alls) on the board.

Suggested Questions Begin Questions A–C as a class.

- *Which team has the highest score?* (Rocket Scientists)

- *Which team has the lowest score?* (Know-It-Alls)

- *How did you decide?* (The Rocket Scientists is the only team with a positive score, which is a score greater than 0. The Know-It-Alls

have the lowest score, because their score of ⁻500 is further "in the hole" than the Super Brains' score of ⁻300.)

- *How many pairs can you make to compare the scores of the three teams?* [Record the list of the needed comparisons (Super Brains vs. Know-It-Alls, Super Brains vs. Rocket Scientists, Know-It-Alls vs. Rocket Scientists) and leave the question for students to answer in their group work.]

- *How could Super Brains get a score of ⁻300 points?* (Possible answer: The Super Brains may have answered a 200-point question correctly and then missed two 250-point questions. This can be written: 200 − 250 − 250 = ⁻300.)

Thinking about these ideas should give the class a good understanding of the context and help them to work through questions.

Small groups are a good organization for the problem.

Explore 1.1

Remind students that, in addition to giving a solution for each question, they will need to explain why they believe their solutions make sense.

Going Further

Suggested Questions Here are some additional questions you can ask.

- *What is the fewest number of questions that each team could have tried to answer to get their current score?* (Super Brains—two questions, Rocket Scientists—one question, Know-It-Alls—two questions)

- *If the Rocket Scientists arrived at their score after answering ten questions, what is a possible sequence of questions they could have answered? Is that the only sequence?*

- *If Rocket Scientists get the next question wrong, would they have a negative score?*

Go over the questions as a class. For Question B, ask the class how they found the difference between the highest and lowest scores. Here are some explanations students have given.

Jonna *We added 500 and 150. The Know-It-Alls are 500 points below 0, and it would take that many points just to get back to 0. The Rocket Scientists are 150 points above 0, so it would take 650 points in all to get from the Know-It-Alls' score to the Rocket Scientists' score.*

Ty *The Super Brains are 300 points in the hole, so they need 300 points to get to 0 and another 150 points to tie the Rocket Scientists. So they are 450 points apart.*

There are many ways each team could have arrived at their score. Have several pairs share their answers to Question C.

For Questions D and E, ask students to explain how they found each team's final score. Here are two explanations students have given.

CeCe *The Super Brains had a score of $^-300$. When they got the 200-point question, their score changed to $^-100$. Then they missed a 150-point question, so their score changed to $^-250$. Next they got a 50-point question, so they went up to $^-200$ points. Then they got another 50-point question, so their score went up again to $^-150$. We wrote the number sentence:*
$$^-300 + 200 - 150 + 50 + 50 = {}^-150.$$

André *We made a table to show what happened to the scores after each question.*

Super Brains

Score	Event	Number Sentence
$^-300$	Win 200	$^-300 + 200 = {}^-100$
$^-100$	Lose 150	$^-100 - 150 = {}^-250$
$^-250$	Win 50	$^-250 + 50 = {}^-200$
$^-200$	Win 50	$^-200 + 50 = {}^-150$

Final Score $= {}^-150$

Rocket Scientists

Score	Event	Number Sentence
150	Lose 50	$150 - 50 = 100$
100	Lose 200	$100 - 200 = {}^-100$
$^-100$	Win 100	$^-100 + 100 = 0$
0	Lose 150	$0 - 150 = {}^-150$

Final Score $= {}^-150$

Know-It-Alls

Score	Event	Number Sentence
$^-500$	Lose 100	$^-500 - 100 = {}^-600$
$^-600$	Win 200	$^-600 + 200 = {}^-400$
$^-400$	Lose 150	$^-400 - 150 = {}^-550$
$^-550$	Lose 50	$^-550 - 50 = {}^-600$

Final Score $= {}^-600$

Once the class agrees on the final scores, discuss the rest of Questions D and E. Ask students to share their ideas about finding the missing information for the number sentences in Question E.

1.1 Playing Math Fever

Mathematical Goals

- Explore the use of and appropriate notation for positive and negative numbers in applied settings
- Interpret and write mathematical sentences

Launch

Discuss the introduction to the Math Fever game.

Post the three scores and begin Questions A–C as a class.

- *Which team has the highest score?*
- *Which team has the lowest score?*
- *How did you decide?*
- *How many pairs can you make to compare the scores of the three teams?*
- *How could Super Brains get a score of ⁻300 points?*

Small groups are a good organization for the problem.

Materials
- Transparencies 1.1A, 1.1B
- Transparency markers

Vocabulary
- negative numbers
- positive numbers
- opposites
- integers
- rational numbers

Explore

Remind students to explain why their solutions make sense.

Going Further

- *What is the fewest number of questions that each team could have tried to answer to get their current score?*
- *If the Rocket Scientists arrived at their score after answering ten questions, what is a possible sequence of questions they could have answered? Is that the only sequence?*
- *If Rocket Scientists get the next question wrong, would they have a negative score?*

Summarize

Go over the questions as a class. For Question B, ask how they found the difference between the highest and lowest scores.

There are many ways each team could have arrived at their score. Have several pairs share their answers to Question C.

For Questions D and E, ask students to explain how they found each team's final score.

Once the class agrees on the final scores, discuss the rest of Questions D and E. Ask students to share their ideas about finding the missing information for the number sentences in Question E.

Materials
- Student notebooks
- Labsheet 1ACE Exercises 31 and 48

ACE Assignment Guide for Problem 1.1

Core 6–8, 48

Other *Applications* 1–5, *Connections* 39

Adapted For suggestions about adapting Exercise 4 and other ACE exercises, see the CMP *Special Needs Handbook*.

Answers to Problem 1.1

A. The Rocket Scientists have the highest score because they have the greatest positive score. The Know-It-Alls have the lowest score because they have the negative score with the greatest absolute value (or it is the furthest to the left of 0).

B. 450 points separate the Super Brains and the Rocket Scientists. 200 points separate the Super Brains and the Know-It-Alls. 650 points separate the Rocket Scientists and the Know-It-Alls.

C. Many answers are possible. Two possible answers for each team's score are provided.

Super Brains: $100 + {}^{-}250 + {}^{-}150 = {}^{-}300$; ${}^{-}250 + 50 + {}^{-}100 = {}^{-}300$

Rocket Scientists: $250 + 50 + {}^{-}150 = 150$; $150 + {}^{-}150 + 150 = 150$

Know-It-Alls: ${}^{-}50 + {}^{-}200 + {}^{-}250 = {}^{-}500$; ${}^{-}100 + {}^{-}250 + {}^{-}150 = {}^{-}500$

D. 1. At this time, students may record an incorrect score as a subtraction or an addition of a negative. One possible answer for each team is provided.

    a. Super Brains:
$${}^{-}300 + 200 + {}^{-}150 + 50 + 50 = {}^{-}150$$

    b. Rocket Scientists:
$$150 + {}^{-}50 + {}^{-}200 + 100 + {}^{-}150 = {}^{-}150$$

    c. Know-It-Alls:
$${}^{-}500 - 100 + 200 - 150 - 50 = {}^{-}600$$

2. The Super Brains and the Rocket Scientists are tied at ${}^{-}150$ points each. The Know-It-Alls have the lowest score.

3. 0 points separate the Super Brains and the Rocket Scientists. 450 points separate the Super Brains and the Know-It-Alls. 450 points separate the Rocket Scientists and the Know-It-Alls.

E. 1. BrainyActs: Answered a 200-point question incorrectly, a 150-point question correctly, and a 100-point question incorrectly for a total score of ${}^{-}150$.

2. MathSperts: Answered a 450-point question correctly and a 200-point question incorrectly for a total score of 250.

3. ExCells: Answered a 200-point question correctly and a 250-point question incorrectly for a total score of ${}^{-}50$.

4. SuperMs: Answered a 350-point question incorrectly and a 200-point question correctly for a total score of ${}^{-}150$. $({}^{-}350 + 200 = {}^{-}150)$

Sample Questions for a Game of Math Fever

If you have the time, play a game of Math Fever with your students. This is not essential as most students understand the situation without taking the time to play the game. Below are some sample questions you can use to play the game with your students.

Fractions

- 50-point question: $\frac{1}{2} + \frac{3}{4} = \blacksquare$ ($\frac{5}{4}$ or $1\frac{1}{4}$)

- 100-point question: $2 - \frac{2}{5} = \blacksquare$ ($\frac{8}{5}$ or $1\frac{3}{5}$)

- 150-point question: $\frac{3}{8} \times \frac{6}{7} = \blacksquare$ ($\frac{18}{56}$ or $\frac{9}{28}$)

- 200-point question: $1\frac{2}{3} - \frac{5}{6} = \blacksquare$ ($\frac{5}{6}$)

- 250-point question: $\frac{5}{7} \div 2\frac{1}{3} = \blacksquare$ ($\frac{15}{49}$)

Similarity

- 50-point question: *How are the perimeters of two similar figures related? Give an example.* (The perimeter of the larger is the scale factor times the perimeter of the smaller figure.)

- 100-point question: *How are the areas of two similar figures related? Give an example.* (The area of the larger figure is the square of the scale factor times the area of the smaller figure.)

- 150-point question: *Rectangle A measures 3 inches by 5 inches. Find the measures of two similar rectangles.* ($6 \times 10, 9 \times 15, 12 \times 20$, etc.)

- 200-point question: *A figure is put in a copier using a copier size factor of 125%. What scale factor and ratio of similarity relate the copy to the original figure?* ($\frac{5}{4}$)

- 250-point question: *What is the minimum number of side and/or angle measurements needed to check the similarity of two triangles?* (If two corresponding angles have the same measure, the third angles will have the same measure and the triangles will be similar. If all three pairs of corresponding sides have the same ratio, the triangles are similar.)

Probability

Use the following information to answer these questions. A bag contains 25 balloons: 15 red, 3 yellow, and 7 orange.

- 50-point question: *What is the theoretical probability of choosing a yellow balloon?* ($\frac{3}{25}$)

- 100-point question: *What is the probability of not choosing a red balloon?* ($\frac{10}{25}$)

- 150-point question: *What is the theoretical probability of getting a yellow or an orange balloon?* ($\frac{10}{25}$)

- 200-point question: *The number of balloons of each color is doubled. What happens to the probability of choosing a red balloon?* ($\frac{15}{25} = \frac{30}{50}$, so the probability is the same.)

- 250-point question: *How many balloons of each color would you need to add to the original bag to make the probability of drawing a red balloon $\frac{1}{2}$?* (Some possibilities: Add 1 yellow and 4 oranges, or 2 yellows and 3 oranges, or 3 yellows and 2 oranges, or 4 yellows and 1 orange, or 5 yellows, or 5 oranges.)

Area and Perimeter

- 50-point question: *A square has a side length of 6 units. Find the area and perimeter.* (The area is 36 square units, and the perimeter is 24 units.)

- 100-point question: *A juice can is about 2.25 inches in diameter. What is its circumference?* (Approximately 7.07 in.)

- 150-point question: *Draw two shapes with perimeters of 18 units but different areas. Give the area of each shape.* (A 2×7 rectangle has a perimeter of 18 units and an area of 14 square units. A 4×5 rectangle has a perimeter of 18 units and an area of 20 square units. Any rectangle whose length and width add to 9 units will work.)

- 200-point question: *Draw two shapes with areas of 25 square units but different perimeters. Give the perimeter of each shape.* (A 5×5 square has an area of 25 square units and a perimeter of 20 units. A 1×25 rectangle has an area of 25 square units, but a perimeter of 52 units.)

- 250-point question: *Find the rectangle with an area of 36 square units and whole-number side lengths that has the smallest perimeter possible.* (6×6)

Tiling the Plane

- 50-point question: *What is another word for tilings?* (tessellations)

- 100-point question: *Which of these shapes work as tiles and which do not? Why?*

(All rectangles and triangles can be used as a tile. A regular hexagon can tile the plane, but not all hexagons can.)

- 150-point question: *Find the dimensions of two possible rectangles that can be made with 36 square tiles.* ($1 \times 36, 2 \times 18, 3 \times 12, 4 \times 9,$ or 6×6)

- 200-point question: *A regular polygon has an angle sum of 1,080°. How many sides does it have?* (8)

- 250-point question: *Use the parallelogram below. Find two ways that copies of it can be used to tile a surface.*

(Using the idea of translations, you can tile the plane with strips of parallelograms arranged so that the top of the parallelogram exactly matches the bottom of a parallelogram in the next strip. You can also offset the strips so that the top of a parallelogram matches the midpoint of the top of a parallelogram in the next strip.)

Factors and Multiples

- 50-point question: *Find two proper factors of 76.* (two of this set: 1, 2, 38, 4, 19)

- 100-point question: *Find all the factors of 171.* (1, 3, 57, 171)

- 150-point question: *Find the least common multiple for 35 and 175.* (175)

- 200-point question: *Find the greatest prime number less than 112.* (109)

- 250-point question: *Find the greatest common factor of 370, 222, and 148.* (74)

1.2 From Sauna to Snowbank

Goals

- Locate positive and negative numbers on a number line

- Compare and order positive and negative numbers

- Understand the relationship between a positive or negative number and its opposite (additive inverse)

This problem continues exploration of the signed numbers, particularly negative numbers, by using one of its most familiar applications: temperatures below 0 on the thermometer.

Launch 1.2

Begin a discussion about different temperatures students have experienced. In addition to outdoor temperatures, you can discuss other temperatures they might experience, such as the temperature of an oven, swimming water, ice cubes, or snow. Some students might know what a sauna or a hot tub is and that a sauna temperature is hot.

You may want to talk about locations of countries and states (referencing a map or a globe) and the hot or cold temperatures people might experience living in those places (e.g., Alaska or Finland vs. California or Mexico).

Suggested Questions

- *What are the hottest and coldest temperatures that you have ever experienced?*

- *How do you show that temperatures are below zero?* (Use a negative sign to show that a temperature is below zero.)

The use of the thermometer motivates translation to use of the number line.

- *On a horizontal number line, where are the positive and negative numbers in relation to 0?* (Positive numbers are to the right of the 0 mark, and negative numbers are to the left of the 0 mark.)

- *You can think of a thermometer as a vertical number line. On a thermometer, where are the positive numbers located in relation to 0?* (above the 0 mark)

- *Where are the negative numbers located in relation to 0?* (below the 0 mark)

- *Suppose the temperature is $^+5°$. Where is $^+5°$ located on this vertical number line in relation to 0?* (5° units above the 0° mark)

- *Suppose the temperature is $^-5°$. Where is $^-5°$ located on this vertical number line in relation to 0?* (5° units below the 0° mark)

Review opposites using the vertical number line (thermometer).

- *Where is the opposite of 12 on a vertical number line?* ($^-12$)

- *Where is the opposite of $^-9$ on a vertical number line?* (9)

Have students begin working this problem individually, and then have them work with partners.

Explore 1.2

As you circulate, have students explain how they are determining their solutions. Encourage students to use sketches of number lines to complete the problems and to show their thinking. A labsheet of number lines is available.

Suggested Questions Ask students to think about the value of numbers as you move on a number line.

- *What happens to the value of numbers as you move from left to right on a number line?* (The numbers increase in value.)

- *What happens to the value of numbers as you move from right to left on a number line?* (The numbers decrease in value.)

Summarize 1.2

Discuss the students' solutions and strategies for the problem.

For Questions B and C, display a thermometer or number line on the overhead or board for students to demonstrate how they found their answers. For Question C, some students may talk about finding the distance between the temperatures and taking half of that distance. Others may use the thermometer and count in equal units from the endpoints to the midpoint. Both are reasonable strategies at this time. If the strategies are not presented by students during the class conversation, present them as options for students to consider.

Suggested Questions For Question D, ask:

- *How many solutions are possible?* (An infinite number; you can always find more fractions in between other fractions.)

For Question E, ask:

- *What would happen to the values of the numbers if we continue the number line to the left?* (The numbers continue to decrease in value.)

- *Which number is less, $^-999$ or $^-1,000$?* ($^-1,000$, because it is further to the left.)

For Question F, students should identify points located the same distance from zero on the opposite side of zero. The sum of a number and its opposite (additive inverse) is zero, $a + {}^-a = 0$.

Absolute value is introduced in Problem 2.2 of the Student Edition. However, if you want to introduce absolute value here, do so. The distance a number is from 0 is called its absolute value. The absolute value of a number is always positive. For example,

$$|^-40| = 40 \text{ and } |^+40| = 40, \text{ so}$$
$$|^-40| = |^+40| = 40.$$

Suggested Questions

- *What is $|^+12|$?* (12)

- *What is $|^-9\frac{1}{2}|$?* ($9\frac{1}{2}$)

1.2 From Sauna to Snowbank

Mathematical Goals

- Locate positive and negative numbers on a number line
- Compare and order positive and negative numbers
- Understand the relationship between a positive or negative number and its opposite (additive inverse)

Launch

Begin a discussion about different temperatures students have experienced.

- *What are the hottest and coldest temperatures that you have ever experienced?*
- *How do you show that temperatures are below zero?*
- *On a horizontal number line, where are the positive and negative numbers in relation to 0?*
- *You can think of a thermometer as a vertical number line. Where are the positive numbers and negative numbers located in relation to 0?*
- *Where is $^+5°$ located on this vertical number line in relation to 0? Where is $^-5°$ located?*
- *Where is the opposite of 12 on a vertical number line? Where is the opposite of $^-9$?*

Have students begin working this problem individually, and then have them work with partners.

Materials
- Transparency 1.2
- Transparency markers
- Number Lines transparency

Vocabulary
- absolute value (optional)

Explore

As you circulate, have students explain how they are determining their solutions. Encourage students to use sketches of number lines. Ask students to think about the value of numbers as you move on a number line.

- *What happens to the value of numbers as you move from left to right on a number line? From right to left?*

Materials
- Number Lines labsheet

Summarize

Discuss the students' solutions and strategies for the problem.

For Questions B and C, display a thermometer or number line for students to demonstrate how they found their answers. For Question C, discuss the strategies of finding the distance between the temperatures and taking half and of using the thermometer to count in from the endpoints.

For Question D, ask:

- *How many solutions are possible?*

Materials
- Student notebooks
- Number Lines or Thermometer transparency

continued on next page

For Question E, ask:

- *What would happen to the values of the numbers if we continue the number line to the left?*
- *Which number is less, ⁻999 or ⁻1,000?*

For Question F, students should identify points located the same distance from zero. The sum of a number and its opposite (additive inverse) is zero,

$$a + {}^-a = 0.$$

Absolute value is introduced in Problem 2.2 of the Student Edition. It can be introduced here. The distance a number is from 0 is called its absolute value. The absolute value of a number is always positive. For example, $|{}^-40| = 40$ and $|{}^+40| = 40$, so $|{}^-40| = |{}^+40| = 40$.

- *What is $|{}^+12|$?*
- *What is $|{}^-9\frac{1}{2}|$?*

ACE Assignment Guide for Problem 1.2

Core 9–19
Other *Connections* 40, 41, 44–47; *Extensions* 49–51; unassigned choices from previous problems

Adapted For suggestions about adapting ACE exercises, see the CMP *Special Needs Handbook*.
Connecting to Prior Units 44–47: *Bits and Pieces I* and *Comparing and Scaling*

Answers to Problem 1.2

A. ⁻40°, ⁻32.7°, ⁻32.5°, ⁻15°, 0°, 113.2°, 115° (Figure 1)

B. 1. 6°F

   2. ⁻7°F and 3°F are the same distance from ⁻2°F.

   3. 2°F

   4. 7°F

C. 1. 5°F   **2.** 5°F   **3.** ⁻5°F
   4. ⁻10°F   **5.** 0°F   **6.** 0°F
   7. ⁻30°F

D. Many answers are possible. For example, ⁻1.5°, ⁻1°, ⁻0.5°, 0°, 0.5°, 0.75° (in order).

E. 1. A = ⁻7
    B = ⁻4
    C = ⁻1.5
    D = 4.5
    E = 6.75

   2. The smaller number is always positioned to the left of the greater number.

F. 1. ⁻3   **2.** ⁻7.5   **3.** $2\frac{2}{3}$

   4. The sum of a number and its opposite is zero. $3 + {}^-3 = 0$; $^-7.5 + 7.5 = 0$.

Figure 1

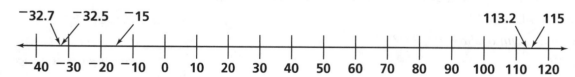

1.3 What's the Change?

Goals

- Write number sentences to reflect the actions and results of changes in situations and find missing values

- Develop and use a number line model for representing addition and subtraction

In Problem 1.2, students began to informally consider the distance between two points on a horizontal number line or a thermometer (vertical number line). In Problem 1.3, they focus on both distance and direction as they seek to describe the change in temperature and write these as number sentences. Number sentences were used in the number units of grade 6.

Launch 1.3

Engage students in a discussion of temperature changes they may have experienced. Some students may recall experiencing the movement of a "cold front," during which the outside temperature drops several degrees, or a quick increase in temperature. Changes are often more subtle with the outside temperature rising and falling in a more predictable way. Most students will be aware that the morning temperatures are often "cooler" than the afternoon temperatures. They may also relate to changes in temperature experienced when they jump into a lake, pool, or the ocean.

Using the context presented in the problem, help students understand that these changes have both *distance* and *direction*. They can consider the reasoning about how to determine distance and direction of change in the given situation. (If you introduced absolute value in the last investigation, you can show students that the absolute value tells the magnitude of change, but the sign tells the direction of change.)

Suggested Questions

- *In the first example, what does the* $^-4$ *represent?* (the starting temperature)

- *What does the* $^+45$ *represent?* (the ending temperature)

- *In the second example, why does* n *equal* $^-14$*?* (The temperature fell 10°. It is a negative change.)

Have students begin working this problem individually, and then have them work with partners.

Explore 1.3

As you circulate, have students explain how they are determining their solutions. Encourage students to use sketches of actions on number lines to show their thinking and to write addition and/or subtraction number sentences to describe their work.

Summarize 1.3

Have students demonstrate and explain their solutions to Questions A–E using horizontal number lines. Take time to consider the number sentences that can be written to describe the actions.

Suggested Questions

- *When you wrote addition sentences, what did the first number represent?* (the starting temperature)

- *What did the second number represent?* (the change in temperature)

- *What did the sum represent?* (the resulting temperature)

In thinking about addition number sentences, it may be helpful to describe the actions as:

Starting Temp. + Change in Temp. = Resulting Temp.

The change will have both distance and direction.

Companion subtraction number sentences that are relevant in some of the problems can be generalized in the same way.

- *When you wrote subtraction sentences, what did the numbers represent?* (Resulting Temp. − Starting Temp. = Change in Temp. OR Resulting Temp. − Change in Temp. = Starting Temp.)

1.3 What's the Change?

Mathematical Goals

- Write number sentences to reflect the actions and results of changes in situations and find missing values
- Develop and use a number line model for representing addition and subtraction

Launch

Engage students in a discussion of temperature changes they may have experienced.

Using the context presented in the problem, help students understand that these changes have both *distance* and *direction*.

- *In the first example, what does the $^-4$ represent?*
- *What does the $^+45$ represent?*
- *In the second example, why does* n *equal* $^-14$?

Have students begin working individually, and then have them work with partners.

Materials

- Transparency 1.3
- Transparency markers

Explore

As you circulate, have students explain how they are determining their solutions.

Encourage students to write addition and/or subtraction number sentences to describe their work.

Materials

- Number Lines labsheet

Summarize

Have students demonstrate and explain their solutions. Take time to consider the number sentences that can be written to describe the actions.

- *When you wrote addition sentences, what did the first addend represent?*
- *What did the second addend represent?*
- *What did the sum represent?*

In thinking about addition number sentences, it may be helpful to describe the actions as:

Starting Temp. + Change in Temp. = Resulting Temp.

The change will have both distance and direction.

Companion subtraction number sentences that are relevant in some of the problems can be generalized in the same way.

- *When you wrote subtraction sentences, what did the numbers represent?*

Resulting Temp. − Starting Temp. = Change in Temp. OR

Resulting Temp. − Change in Temp. = Starting Temp.

Materials

- Student notebooks
- Number Lines transparency
- Labsheet 1ACE Exercises 31 and 48

ACE Assignment Guide for Problem 1.3

Differentiated Instruction
Solutions for All Learners

Core 20–29

Other *Applications* 30, 31; *Connections* 42, 43; unassigned choices from previous problems

Adapted For suggestions about adapting ACE exercises, see the CMP *Special Needs Handbook*.

Answers to Problem 1.3

A. $120° + n = ^-20°$ or $120° + ^-140° = ^-20°$ (Figure 2)

B. **1.** $25° + 10° = 35°$

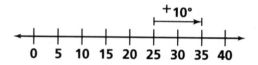

2. $25° + ^-2° = 23°$ or $25° - 2° = 23°$ (Figure 3)

3. $25° + ^-30° = ^-5°$ or $25° - 30° = ^-5°$

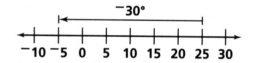

C. **1.** $^-15° + 3° = ^-12°$ (Figure 4)

2. $^-15° + ^-10° = ^-25°$

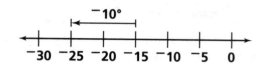

3. $^-15° + 40° = 25°$ (Figure 5)

D. **Note:** It is very important that students write number sentences, not just find the temperature differences. Check students' number lines.

1. $20° + n = ^-10°$ or $20° + ^-30° = ^-10°$

2. $^-20° + n = ^-10°$ or $^-20° + 10° = ^-10°$

3. $^-20° + n = 10°$ or $^-20° + 30° = 10°$

4. $^-10° + n = ^-20°$ or $^-10° + ^-10° = ^-20°$

5. $20° + n = 10°$ or $20° + ^-10° = 10°$

6. $10° + n = 20°$ or $10° + 10° = 20°$

E. Check students' number lines.
$^-5° + 20° + ^-25° + 40° + ^-70° = ^-40°$

Figure 2

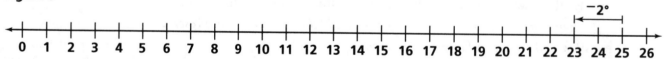

Figure 3

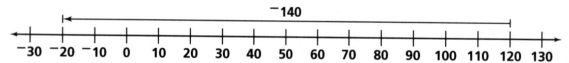

Figure 4

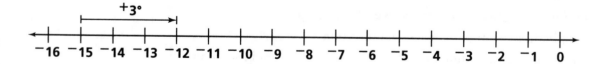

Figure 5

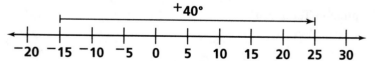

1.4 In the Chips

Goals

- Develop and use a chip model for representing addition and subtraction
- Interpret and write mathematical sentences

A final model for work with integers is the "chip model," where black chips represent positive numbers ("in the black") and red chips represent negative numbers ("in the red"). This problem promotes informal experiences with addition and subtraction of signed numbers. Investigation 2 will formalize algorithms for completing these operations. Note that this model is a representation of integer arithmetic, while the directed distance model from Problem 1.3 is a continuous model that can represent fraction and decimal numbers and lengths.

Mathematics Background

For background on chip models, see page 5.

In the chip model, integers may be represented using different combinations of chips. For example, $^-5$ can be shown with 5 red chips ($^-5 = ^-5$), with 7 red chips and 2 black chips ($^-5 = ^-7 + ^+2$), or with 10 red chips and 5 black chips ($^-5 = ^-10 + ^+5$). It is this flexibility in "renaming" integers using different combinations of positive/negative numbers that is helpful in representing subtraction.

Subtraction involves representing a quantity with chips and then removing ("taking away") the number of chips necessary. (Figure 6)

Launch 1.4

Discuss the context of describing finances as "in the black" or "in the red." Check to see if your students have ever heard these terms used and in what context.

Students may be able to share stories of saving money in order to make a purchase. Or they may recall borrowing against future income (e.g., their allowance or money from a babysitting job) in order to buy a gift. They should be able to identify situations where they have been "in the black" and "in the red."

Use Julia's method using chips and a chip board to introduce the chip model for solving problems.

Suggested Questions Discuss with students the other chip problems in the Getting Ready.

- *The board has 3 red chips. Five black chips are added. What is the end result?* ($^+2$)

- *What number sentence represents this situation?* ($^-3 + {}^+5 = {}^+2$.)

Continue asking students about the missing parts.

Answers to Getting Ready

2. End with: 2 black chips; $^-2 + {}^+1 - {}^-3 = {}^+2$

3. Rule: Subtract 4 red chips; $^-6 - {}^-4 = {}^-2$

4. Start with: 1 black chip; $^+1 - {}^-3 = {}^+4$

Have students work with partners.

Figure 6

Problem	Show	Remove	Answer
$^+7 - {}^+5$	7 black	5 black	$^+7 - {}^+5 = {}^+2$
$^-8 - {}^-3$	8 red	3 red	$^-8 - {}^-3 = {}^-5$
$^+7 - {}^-2$	9 black and 2 red	2 red	$^+7 - {}^-2 = ({}^+9 + {}^-2) - {}^-2 = {}^+9$
$^-5 - {}^-7$	7 red and 2 black	7 red	$^-5 - {}^-7 = ({}^+2 + {}^+7) - {}^-7 = {}^+2$
$^-4 - {}^+2$	6 red and 2 black	2 black	$^-4 - {}^+2 = ({}^-6 + {}^+2) - {}^+2 = {}^-6$
$^+3 - {}^+7$	7 black and 4 red	7 black	$^+3 - {}^+7 = ({}^-4 + {}^+7) - {}^+7 = {}^-4$

Explore 1.4

As you circulate, have students explain how they are determining their solutions.

Encourage students to use chips and the chip board to show their thinking. Have them write addition and/or subtraction number sentences to describe their work.

Summarize 1.4

Have students demonstrate and explain their solutions to Questions A–E, using chips to help explain their reasoning. Take time to discuss the number sentences that can be written to describe the actions.

Suggested Question

• *How are the number line model and the chip model alike?* (They both help you make sense of adding and subtracting with negative numbers. When adding, you can think of them in similar ways. The first number tells the starting amount or location on the number line for the number line model and it tells how much is on the board with the chip model. The second number tells the amount to move on the number line and in which direction. It tells the number and color of chips to put on, or remove from, the board.

1.4 In the Chips

Mathematical Goals

- Interpret and write mathematical sentences
- Develop and use a chip model for representing addition and subtraction

Launch

Discuss the context of describing finances as "in the black" or "in the red." Have students identify situations where they have been "in the black" and "in the red."

Use Julia's method using chips and a chip board to introduce the chip model for solving problems.

Discuss with students the other chip problems in the Getting Ready.

- *The board has 3 red chips. Five black chips are added. What is the end result?*
- *What number sentence represents this situation?*

Continue asking students about the missing parts.

Answers to Getting Ready

2. End with: 2 black chips; $^-2 + {}^+1 - {}^-3 = {}^+2$

3. Rule: Subtract 4 red chips; $^-6 - {}^-4 = {}^-2$

4. Start with: 1 black chip; $^+1 - {}^-3 = {}^+4$

Have students work with partners.

Materials

- Transparencies 1.4A, 1.4B
- Chip Boards transparency
- Chips or tiles in two colors
- Transparency markers

Explore

As you circulate, have students explain how they are determining their solutions.

Encourage students to use chips and the chip board to show their thinking. Have them write addition and/or subtraction number sentences to describe their work.

Materials

- Chip Boards labsheet
- Chips or tiles in two colors

Summarize

Have students demonstrate and explain their solutions using chips.

Take time to consider the number sentences that can be written to describe the actions.

- *How are the number line model and the chip model alike?*

Materials

- Student notebooks

ACE Assignment Guide for Problem 1.4

Differentiated Instruction
Solutions for All Learners

Core 36, 37
Other *Connections* 32–35, 38; *Extensions* 52–54; unassigned choices from previous problems

Adapted For suggestions about adapting ACE exercises, see the CMP *Special Needs Handbook*.

Answers to Problem 1.4

A. Answers will vary. One answer for each is provided below.

1. 3 black + 3 red = 0; or $^+3 + \, ^-3 = 0$

2. 15 black + 3 red = 12 black; or $^+15 + \, ^-3 = \, ^+12$

3. 1 black + 8 red = 7 red; or $^+1 + \, ^-8 = \, ^-7$

4. 125 black + 250 red = 125 red; or $^+125 + \, ^-250 = \, ^-125$

B.
1. $^+8 + \, ^-12 = \, ^-4$
2. $(^+8 + \, ^-12) + \, ^+5 = \, ^+1$ or $^-4 + \, ^+5 = \, ^+1$
3. $(^+8 + \, ^-12) - \, ^-5 = \, ^+1$ or $^-4 - \, ^-5 = \, ^+1$
4. $(^+8 + \, ^-12) - \, ^+3 = \, ^-7$ or $^-4 - 3 = \, ^-7$
5. $(^+8 + \, ^-12) + \, ^-3 = \, ^-7$ or $^-4 + \, ^-3 = \, ^-7$

C. Start with 7 red chips and add 5 black chips for a value of 2 red chips.

$^-7 + \, ^+5 = \, ^-2$

After paying her sister, Cybil has $0 and still owes her sister $2.

D. Students start with 10 black chips. Because you can't take away chips that aren't already on the board, students must discover ways to represent 15 black chips without changing the value of 10 black chips. They could add 5 red chips and 5 black chips to the board because their total value is zero. Once the 15 black chips are taken away, 5 red chips remain. The result should leave 5 more red chips than black.

$^+10 - \, ^+15 = \, ^+10 + \, ^+5 + \, ^-5 - \, ^+15 = \, ^-5$

E.
1. Represent $^+3$ with 3 black chips; remove 2 black chips; leaves 1 black chip, or $^+1$.

2. Represent $^-4$ with 6 red chips and two black chips; remove 2 black chips; leaves 6 red chips, or $^-6$.

3. Represent $^-4$ with 4 red chips; remove 2 red chips; leaves 2 red chips, or $^-2$.

4. Represent $^+7$ with 7 black chips; add 6 red chips; remove 6 black and 6 red chips; leaves 1 black chip, or $^+1$.

5. Represent $^-3$ with 3 red chips; add 5 red chips and 5 black chips; remove 5 black chips; leaves 8 red chips, or $^-8$.

6. You are looking for the number of chips so that if you take away 2 red chips, you have 6 black chips remaining. Put 6 black chips on the board, add 2 red chips, and pair 2 red chips with 2 black chips. Your starting number is what is left: 4 black chips, or $^+4$.

Extending the Number System

In your study of numbers, you have focused on operations (+, −, ×, and ÷) with whole numbers, fractions, and decimals. In this unit, you will learn about some important new numbers in the number system.

Suppose you start with a number line showing 0, 1, 2, 3, 4, and 5.

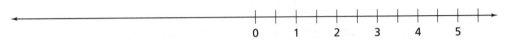

Take the number line and fold it around the zero point. Make marks on the left side of zero to match the marks on the right side.

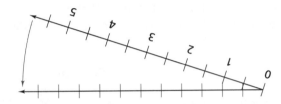

Label the new marks with numbers that have negative signs (⁻). These numbers (to the left of 0) are **negative numbers.**

I owe my Dad 3 dollars, so I have ⁻3 dollars.

Investigation 1 Extending the Number System **5**

Notes _____

_____

_____

_____

Each negative number is paired with a positive number. The numbers in the pair are the same distance from zero but in opposite directions on the number line. These number pairs are called opposites. You can label positive numbers with positive signs (+).

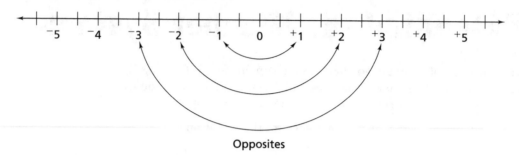

Opposites

Some subsets of the positive and negative numbers have special names. Whole numbers and their opposites are called integers (⁻4, ⁻3, ⁻2, ⁻1, 0, ⁺1, ⁺2, ⁺3, ⁺4).

Fractions also have opposites. For example, $^+\frac{1}{2}$ and $^-\frac{1}{2}$ are opposites. Positive and negative integers and fractions are called rational numbers. Rational numbers are numbers that can be expressed as one integer divided by another integer.

Examples

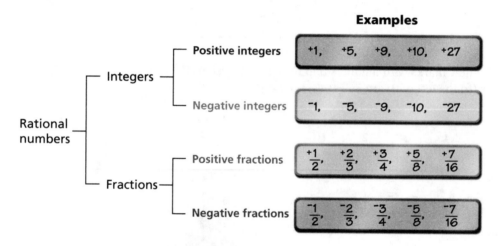

Notes _____

_____

_____

_____

In mathematical notation, you can write a positive number with a raised plus sign ($^+150$) or without any sign (150). You can write a negative number with a raised minus sign ($^-150$). To avoid confusion with operation signs, it is common to use raised signs.

Many calculators have a special negative number key . When you press 5 ⊟ ⊝ 2, the calculator shows "5 − $^-$2."

Getting Ready for Problem 1.1

- Where would the following pairs of numbers be located on the number line?

  $^+7$ and $^-7$

  $^+2.7$ and $^-2.7$

  $^-3.8$ and $^+3.8$

  $-\frac{1}{2}$ and $^+\frac{1}{2}$

  $4\frac{3}{4}$ and $^-4\frac{3}{4}$

- If the same relationship holds true for all numbers, what would be the opposite of $^-1\frac{2}{3}$ and where would it be located?

Notes _____

_____

_____

_____

1.1 Playing Math Fever

Ms. Bernoski's math classes often play Math Fever, a game similar to a popular television game show. The game board is shown. Below each category name are five cards. The front of each card shows a point value. The back of each card has a question related to the category. Cards with higher point values have more difficult questions.

Math Fever

Operations With Fractions	Similarity	Probability	Area and Perimeter	Tiling the Plane	Factors and Multiples
50	50	50	50	50	50
100	100	100	100	100	100
150	150	150	150	150	150
200	200	200	200	200	200
250	250	250	250	250	250

The game is played in teams. One team starts the game by choosing a card. The teacher asks the question on the back of the card. The first team to answer the question correctly gets the point value on the card. The card is then removed from the board. If a team answers the question incorrectly, the point value is subtracted from their score. The team that answers correctly chooses the next category and point value.

Notes _____

_____

_____

_____

Problem 1.1 Using Positive and Negative Numbers

At one point in a game, the scores are as follows:

Super Brains	Rocket Scientists	Know-It-Alls
$^-300$	150	$^-500$

A. Which team has the highest score? Which team has the lowest score? Explain.

B. What is the difference in points for each pair of teams?

C. Use number sentences to describe two possible ways that each team reached its score.

D. The current scores are $^-300$ for Super Brains, 150 for Rocket Scientists, and $^-500$ for Know-It-Alls.

  1. Write number sentences to represent each sequence of points. Start with the current score for each team.

a. Super Brains

Point Value	Answer
200	Correct
150	Incorrect
50	Correct
50	Correct

b. Rocket Scientists

Point Value	Answer
50	Incorrect
200	Incorrect
100	Correct
150	Incorrect

c. Know-It-Alls

Point Value	Answer
100	Incorrect
200	Correct
150	Incorrect
50	Incorrect

  2. Now which team has the highest score? Which team has the lowest score?

  3. What is the difference in points for each pair of teams?

E. The number sentences below describe what happens at a particular point during a game of Math Fever. Find each missing number. Explain what each sentence tells about a team's performance and overall score.

  1. BrainyActs: $^-200 + 150 - 100 = \blacksquare$

  2. MathSperts: $450 - 200 = \blacksquare$

  3. ExCells: $200 - 250 = \blacksquare$

  4. SuperMs: $^-350 + \blacksquare = {}^-150$

ACE Homework starts on page 16.

Notes

_____

_____

_____

_____

1.2 From Sauna to Snowbank

The record high and low temperatures in the United States are 134°F in Death Valley, California and ⁻80°F in Prospect Creek, Alaska. Imagine going from 134°F to ⁻80°F in an instant!

In Finland, people think that such temperature shocks are fun and good for your health. This activity is called sauna-bathing.

In the winter, Finnish people sit for a certain amount of time in sauna houses. The houses are heated as high as 120°F. Then the people run outside, where the temperature might be as low as ⁻20°F.

Inside the Sauna   **Outside in Snow**

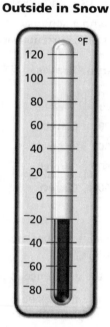

The two thermometers shown are similar to number lines. One horizontal number line can show the same information as the two thermometers.

Notes _____

_____

_____

_____

On the number line, a move to the left is a move in a negative direction. The numbers decrease in value. A move to the right is a move in a positive direction. The numbers increase in value. On the thermometers, a move down means the number values decrease and the temperatures get colder. A move up means the number values increase and the temperatures get hotter.

Problem 1.2 Comparing and Ordering Positive and Negative Numbers

Sketch number lines to show your reasoning.

A. Order these temperatures from least to greatest.

0°F   115°F   ⁻15°F   ⁻32.5°F   ⁻40°F   113.2°F   ⁻32.7°F

B. For each pair of temperatures, identify which temperature is further from ⁻2°F.

1. 6°F or ⁻6°F?   **2.** ⁻7°F or 3°F?

3. 2°F or ⁻5°F?   **4.** ⁻10°F or 7°F?

C. Identify the temperature that is halfway between each pair of temperatures.

1. 0°F and 10°F   **2.** ⁻5°F and 15°F

3. 5°F and ⁻15°F   **4.** 0°F and ⁻20°F

5. ⁻8°F and 8°F   **6.** ⁻6°F and 6°F

7. During one week, the high temperature was 60°F. The halfway temperature was 15°F. What was the low temperature?

D. Name six temperatures between ⁻2°F and ⁺1°F. Order them from least to greatest.

E. 1. Estimate values for points A–E.

2. How does the number line help you find the smaller value of two numbers?

F. What are the opposites of these numbers?

1. 3   **2.** 7.5   **3.** $-2\frac{2}{3}$

4. What is the sum of a number and its opposite?

ACE **Homework starts on page 16.**

Investigation 1 Extending the Number System   **11**

Notes _____

_____

_____

_____

Did You Know?

In golf, scores can be negative. Each golf hole has a value called par. Par is the number of strokes a golfer usually needs to complete the hole. For example, a good golfer, like Vijay Singh, should be able to complete a par 4 hole in four strokes. If a golfer completes the hole in six strokes, then his or her score for that hole is "two over par" ($^+2$). If a golfer completes the hole in two strokes, his or her score is "two under par" ($^-2$). A player's score for a round of golf is the total of the number of strokes above or under par.

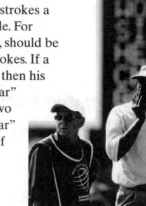

Go Online

PHSchool.com   **For:** Information about golf
Web Code: ane-9031

1.3 What's the Change?

The National Weather Service keeps records of temperature changes.

The world record for fastest rise in outside air temperature occurred in Spearfish, South Dakota, on January 22, 1943. The temperature rose from $^-4°$F to 45°F in two minutes.

What was the change in temperature over that two minutes? How could you show this change, n, on the number line?

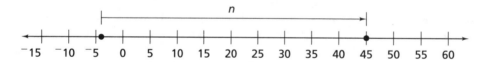

From $^-4°$F to 0°F is a change of $^+4°$F, and from 0°F to 45°F is a change of $^+45°$F. So the total change is $^+49°$F. The following number sentences show this.

$$^-4 + n = {}^+45$$
$$^-4 + {}^+49 = {}^+45$$

The sign of the change in temperature shows the direction of the change. In this case, $^+49$ means the temperature increased 49°F.

12   Accentuate the Negative

Notes

If the temperature had instead dropped 10° from ⁻4°F, you would write the change as ⁻10°F.

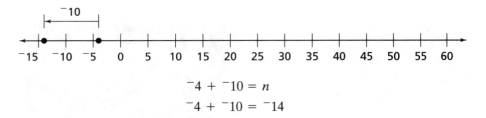

$$^-4 + {^-10} = n$$
$$^-4 + {^-10} = {^-14}$$

Problem 1.3 Using a Number Line Model

Sketch number lines and write number sentences for each question.

A. A person goes from a sauna at 120°F to an outside temperature of ⁻20°F. What is the change in temperature?

B. The temperature reading on a thermometer is 25°F. In the problems below, a positive number means the temperature is rising. A negative number means the temperature is falling. What is the new reading for each temperature change below?

  1. ⁺10°F   **2.** ⁻2°F   **3.** ⁻30°F

C. The temperature reading on a thermometer is ⁻15°F. What is the new reading for each temperature change?

  1. ⁺3°F   **2.** ⁻10°F   **3.** ⁺40°F

D. What is the change in temperature when the thermometer reading moves from the first temperature to the second temperature? Write an equation for each part.

  1. 20°F to ⁻10°F   **2.** ⁻20°F to ⁻10°F

  3. ⁻20°F to 10°F   **4.** ⁻10°F to ⁻20°F

  5. 20°F to 10°F   **6.** 10°F to 20°F

E. The temperature was ⁻5°F when Sally went to school on Monday. The temperature rose 20°F during the day, but fell 25°F during the night. A heat wave the next day increased the temperature 40°F. But an arctic wind overnight decreased the temperature 70°F! What was the temperature after the 70° decrease?

ACE   **Homework starts on page 16.**

STUDENT PAGE

Notes _____

_____

_____

_____

1.4 In the Chips

When business records were kept by hand, accountants used red ink for expenses and black ink for income. If your income was greater than your expenses you were "in the black." If your expenses were greater than your income you were "in the red."

Julia has this problem to solve:

> Linda owes her sister $6 for helping her cut the lawn. She earns $4 delivering papers with her brother. Is she "in the red" or "in the black"?

Getting Ready for Problem 1.4

Julia uses red and black chips to model income and expenses. Each black chip represents $^{+}1$ dollar of income. Each red chip represents $^{-}1$ dollar of income (expenses).

Julia puts chips on the board to represent the situation. She decides Linda is "in the red" 2 dollars, or $^{-}2$ dollars.

Julia's Chip Board

- Why do you think she concludes that $^{-}6 + {^{+}4} = {^{-}2}$?
- What is another way to show $^{-}2$ on the board?

14   Accentuate the Negative

STUDENT PAGE

(14) 32

Notes _____

Find the missing part for each chip problem. What would be a number sentence for each problem?

	Start With	Rule	End With
1.	●●●	Add 5 ●	▪
2.	●●●	Subtract 3 ●	▪
3.	●●● ●●●	▪	●●
4.	▪	Subtract 3 ●	●●●●

Problem 1.4 Using a Chip Model

Use ideas about black and red chips to answer each question. Then write a number sentence.

A. Give three combinations of red and black chips (using at least one of each color) that will equal each value.

   1. 0   **2.** $^{+}12$ **3.** $^{-}7$ **4.** $^{-}125$

B. Use this chip board as the starting value for each part. Find the total value on each chip board.

   1. original chip board

   2. add 5 black chips

   3. remove 5 red chips

   4. remove 3 black chips

   5. add 3 red chips

C. Cybil owes her sister $7. Her aunt pays her $5 to walk her dog. How much money does she have after she pays her sister?

D. Tate earns $10 mowing a lawn. He needs to pay $15 to rent his equipment. How much more money does he need to pay his rent?

E. Describe chip board displays that would match these number sentences. Find the results in each case.

   1. $^{+}3 - {}^{+}2 = $ ▪   **2.** $^{-}4 - {}^{+}2 = $ ▪   **3.** $^{-}4 - {}^{-}2 = $ ▪

   4. $^{+}7 + $ ▪ $ = {}^{+}1$ **5.** $^{-}3 - {}^{+}5 = $ ▪   **6.** ▪ $ - {}^{-}2 = {}^{+}6$

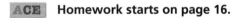

active math
online
For: Interactive Chip Model
Visit: PHSchool.com
Web Code: and-4104

ACE Homework starts on page 16.

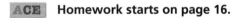

Investigation 1 Extending the Number System   **15**

Notes _____

_____

_____

_____

Applications

Describe a sequence of five correct or incorrect answers that would produce each Math Fever score.

1. Super Brains: 300

2. Rocket Scientists: ⁻200

3. Know-It-Alls: ⁻250

4. Teacher's Pets: 0

5. Multiple Choice Which order is from least to greatest?

A. 300, 0, ⁻200, ⁻250

B. ⁻250, ⁻200, 0, 300

C. 0, ⁻200, ⁻250, 300

D. ⁻200, ⁻250, 300, 0

Find each Math Fever team's score. Write number sentences for each team. Assume that each team starts with 0 points.

6. Protons

Point Value	Answer
250	Correct
100	Correct
200	Correct
150	Incorrect
200	Incorrect

7. Neutrons

Point Value	Answer
200	Incorrect
50	Correct
250	Correct
150	Incorrect
50	Incorrect

8. Electrons

Point Value	Answer
50	Incorrect
200	Incorrect
100	Correct
200	Correct
150	Incorrect

For each set of rational numbers in Exercises 9 and 10, draw a number line and locate the points. Remember to choose an appropriate scale.

9. $-\frac{2}{8}$, $\frac{1}{4}$, ⁻1.5, $1\frac{3}{4}$

10. ⁻1.25, $-\frac{1}{3}$, 1.5, $-\frac{1}{6}$

11. Order the numbers from least to greatest.

23.6   ⁻45.2   50   ⁻0.5   0.3 $\frac{3}{5}$ $-\frac{4}{5}$

For: Help with Exercise 11
Web Code: ane-4111

Notes _____

_____

_____

_____

Copy each pair of numbers in Exercises 12–19. Insert <, >, or = to make
a true statement.

12. 3 ■ 0

13. ⁻23.4 ■ 23.4

14. 46 ■ ⁻79

15. ⁻75 ■ ⁻90

16. ⁻300 ■ 100

17. ⁻1,000 ■ ⁻999

18. ⁻1.73 ■ ⁻1.730

19. ⁻4.3 ■ ⁻4.03

Go Online
PHSchool.com

For: Multiple-Choice Skills
Practice
Web Code: ana-4154

For Exercises 20–29, follow the steps using the number line. What is the
final position?

20. Start at 8. Add ⁻7.

21. Start at ⁻8. Add 10.

22. Start at ⁻3. Add ⁻5.

23. Start at 7. Add ⁻7.

24. Start at ⁻2. Add 12.

25. Start at 3. Subtract 5.

26. Start at ⁻2. Subtract 2.

27. Start at 4. Subtract 7.

28. Start at 0. Subtract 5.

29. Start at ⁻8. Subtract 3.

30. The greatest one-day temperature change in world records occurred
at Browning, Montana (bordering Glacier National Park), from
January 23–24 in 1916. The temperature fell from 44°F to ⁻56°F in
less than 24 hours.

a. What was the temperature change that day?

b. Write a number sentence to represent the temperature change.

c. Show the temperature change on a number line.

Investigation 1 Extending the Number System   **17**

Notes _____

_____

_____

_____

31. Find the value for each labeled point on the number line. Then use the values to calculate each change.

a. A to B   **b.** A to C   **c.** B to C   **d.** C to A   **e.** B to A

Find the missing part for each situation.

	Start With	Rule	End With
32.	●●●	Add 5 ●	▪
33.	●●●	Subtract 3 ●	▪
34.	●●●●●	▪	●●
35.	▪	Subtract 3 ●	●●●●

36. Write a story problem for this situation. Find the value represented by the chips on the board.

For Exercises 37 and 38, use the chip board in Exercise 36.

37. Describe three different ways to change the numbers of black and red chips, but leave the value of the board unchanged.

38. Start with the original board. What is the new value of chips on the board when you

   a. remove 3 red chips?

   b. and then add 3 black chips?

   c. and then add 200 black chips and 195 red chips?

Notes _____

_____

_____

_____

Connections

39. In a football game, one team makes seven plays in the first quarter. The results of those plays are (in order): gain of 7 yards, gain of 2 yards, loss of 5 yards, loss of 12 yards, gain of 16 yards, gain of 8 yards, loss of 8 yards.

  a. What is the overall gain (or loss) from all seven plays?

  b. What is the average gain (or loss) per play?

Find the number of strokes above or under par for each player. See the Did You Know? before the introduction to Problem 1.3 for the definition of par. Write number sentences with positive and negative numbers to show each result.

	Player	Round 1	Round 2	Round 3	Round 4
40.	Tiger Woods	4 over par	6 under par	3 under par	1 over par
41.	Karrie Webb	2 under par	1 under par	5 over par	5 under par

For Exercises 42 and 43, use the following information. The highest point on earth is the top of Mount Everest. It is 29,035 feet above sea level. The lowest exposed land is the shore of the Dead Sea. It is 1,310 feet below sea level.

42. Multiple Choice What is the change in elevation from the top of Everest to the shore of the Dead Sea?

  F. $^{-}$30,345 feet
  G. $^{-}$27,725 feet
  H. 27,725 feet
  J. 30,345 feet

43. Multiple Choice What is the change in elevation from the shore of the Dead Sea to the top of Everest?

  A. $^{-}$30,345 feet
  B. $^{-}$27,725 feet
  C. 27,725 feet
  D. 30,345 feet

Order the numbers from least to greatest.

44. $\frac{2}{5}, \ \frac{3}{10}, \ \frac{5}{9}, \ \frac{9}{25}$

45. 20.33, 2.505, 23.30, 23

46. 1.52, $1\frac{4}{7}$, 2, $\frac{9}{6}$

47. 3, $\frac{19}{6}$, $2\frac{8}{9}$, 2.95

Notes _____

_____

_____

_____

Extensions

48. At the start of December, Kenji had a balance of $595.50 in his checking account. The following is a list of transactions he made during the month.

Date	Transaction	Balance
December 1		$595.50
December 5	Writes a check for $19.95	
December 12	Writes a check for $280.88	
December 15	Deposits $257.00	
December 17	Writes a check for $58.12	
December 21	Withdraws $50.00	
December 24	Writes checks for $17.50, $41.37, and $65.15	
December 26	Deposits $100.00	
December 31	Withdraws $50.00	

a. Copy and complete the table.

b. What was Kenji's balance at the end of December?

c. When was his balance the greatest?

d. When was his balance the least?

Find the missing temperature information in each situation.

49. The high temperature is 20°C. The low temperature is ⁻15°C. What temperature is halfway between the high and the low?

50. The low temperature is ⁻8°C. The temperature halfway between the high and the low is 5°C. What is the high temperature?

51. The high temperature is ⁻10°C. The low temperature is ⁻15°C. What is the temperature halfway between the high and the low?

Find values for A and B that make each mathematical sentence true.

52. $^{+}A + {}^{-}B = {}^{-}1$

53. $^{-}A + {}^{+}B = 0$

54. $^{-}A - {}^{-}B = {}^{-}2$

Notes _____

_____

_____

_____

Mathematical Reflections

In this investigation, you learned ways to order and operate with positive and negative numbers. The following questions will help you summarize what you have learned.

Think about your answers to these questions. Discuss your ideas with other students and your teacher. Then write a summary of your findings in your notebook.

1. How do you decide which of two numbers is greater when

   a. both numbers are positive?

   b. both numbers are negative?

   c. one number is positive and one number is negative?

2. What does comparing locations of numbers on a number line tell you about the numbers?

Notes _____

_____

_____

_____

Investigation

ACE
Assignment Choices

Differentiated Instruction
Solutions for All Learners

Problem 1.1
Core 6–8, 48
Other *Applications 1–5, Connections 39*

Problem 1.2
Core 9–19
Other *Connections 40, 41, 44–47; Extensions 49–51;*
unassigned choices from previous problems

Problem 1.3
Core 20–29
Other *Applications 30, 31; Connections 42, 43;*
unassigned choices from previous problems

Problem 1.4
Core 36, 37
Other *Applications 10; Connections 32–35, 38;
Extensions 52–54;* unassigned choices from
previous problems

Adapted For suggestions about adapting
Exercise 4 and other ACE exercises, see the
CMP *Special Needs Handbook.*
Connecting to Prior Units 44–47: *Bits and Pieces I*
and *Comparing and Scaling*

Applications

1–4. Answers will vary. Possible answers given.

1. The Super Brains answered a 250-point
question correctly, a 50-point question
incorrectly, a 100-point question correctly, a
200-point question incorrectly, and a
200-point question correctly.

$250 + {}^-50 + 100 + {}^-200 + 200 = 300$

2. The Rocket Scientists answered a 50-point
question correctly, a 150-point question
correctly, a 100-point question incorrectly, a
150-point question incorrectly, and a
150-point question incorrectly.

$50 + 150 + {}^-100 + {}^-150 + {}^-150 = {}^-200$

3. The Know-It-Alls answered a 50-point
question correctly, a 100-point question
incorrectly, a 150-point question incorrectly, a
100-point question incorrectly, and a 50-point
question correctly.

$50 + {}^-100 + {}^-150 + {}^-100 + 50 = {}^-250$

4. The Teacher's Pets answered a 100-point
question correctly, a 200-point question
correctly, a 150-point question incorrectly, a
200-point question incorrectly, and a 50-point
question correctly.

$100 + 200 + {}^-150 + {}^-200 + 50 = 0$

5. B

6. $250 + 100 + 200 + {}^-150 + {}^-200 = 200$ or
$250 + 100 + 200 - 150 - 200 = 200$

7. ${}^-200 + 50 + 250 + {}^-150 + {}^-50 = {}^-100$ or
${}^-200 + 50 + 250 - 150 - 50 = {}^-100$

8. ${}^-50 + {}^-200 + 100 + 200 + {}^-150 = {}^-100$ or
${}^-50 - 200 + 100 + 200 - 150 = {}^-100$

9.

10.

11. ${}^-45.2, \; {}^-\frac{4}{5}, \; {}^-0.5, \; 0.3, \; \frac{3}{5}, \; 23.6, \; 50$

12. $3 > 0$ 13. ${}^-23.4 < 23.4$

14. $46 > {}^-79$ 15. ${}^-75 > {}^-90$

16. ${}^-300 < 100$ 17. ${}^-1,000 < {}^-999$

18. ${}^-1.73 = {}^-1.730$ 19. ${}^-4.3 < {}^-4.03$

20. 1   21. 2

22. ${}^-8$ 23. 0

24. 10   25. ${}^-2$

26. ${}^-4$ 27. ${}^-3$

28. ${}^-5$ 29. ${}^-11$

30. a. It fell by 100° ($^-100°$).
$^-56° - 44° = {}^-100°$

b. $^-56° - 44° = {}^-100°$ or
$44° + {}^-100° = {}^-56°$

c. (Figure 7)

31. a. The change from A to B is 15 units.
$^-25 + \blacksquare = {}^-10$ or $^-10 - {}^-25 = \blacksquare$;
$\blacksquare = 15$

b. The change from A to C is 45 units.
$^-25 + \blacksquare = {}^+20$ or $^+20 - {}^-25 = \blacksquare$;
$\blacksquare = {}^+45$

c. The change from B to C is 30 units.
$^-10 + \blacksquare = {}^+20$ or $^+20 - {}^-10 = \blacksquare$;
$\blacksquare = {}^+30$

d. The change from C to A is $^-45$ units.
$^+20 + \blacksquare = {}^-25$ or $^-25 - {}^+20 = \blacksquare$;
$\blacksquare = {}^-45$

e. The change from B to A is $^-15$ units.
$^-10 + \blacksquare = {}^-25$ or $^-25 - {}^-10 = \blacksquare$;
$\blacksquare = {}^-15$

32. End with: 2 red chips

33. End with: 2 red chips

34. Add: 3 black chips or Subtract: 3 red chips.

35. Start with: any combination equivalent to 1 red chip

36. Answers will vary. Possible answer: Julia earned $5 mowing her neighbor's yard, but she spent $8 on gas; $^-8 + {}^+5 = {}^-3$

37. Answers will vary; however, it is important for students to recognize that it is the opposite pairs ($^+1 + {}^-1$) that are used to change the number of chips but keep the total value the same. For example, one can add 2 pairs of black and red chips and still leave the value of the board unchanged ($^+7 + {}^-10 = {}^-3$). One can also remove 4 pairs of black and red chips and still leave the value of the board unchanged ($^+1 + {}^-4 = {}^-3$).

38. a. 0; 8 original red chips $-$ 3 red chips = 5 red chips remaining; $^+5 + {}^-5 = 0$

b. $^+3$; 5 original black chips + 3 black chips = 8 black chips; $^+8 + {}^-5 = {}^+3$

c. $^+8$; 8 black chips + 200 black chips = 208 black chips; 5 red chips + 195 red chips = 200 red chips; $^+208 + {}^-200 = {}^+8$

Connections

39. a. gain of 8 yds;
$^+7 + {}^+2 + {}^-5 + {}^-12 + {}^+16 + {}^+8 + {}^-8 = {}^+8$

b. about 1.14 yd per play; $8 \div 7 \approx 1.14$

40. 4 below par; $^+4 + {}^-6 + {}^-3 + {}^+1 = {}^-4$

41. 3 below par; $^-2 + {}^-1 + {}^+5 + {}^-5 = {}^-3$

42. F

43. D

44. $\frac{3}{10}, \frac{9}{25}, \frac{2}{5}, \frac{5}{9}$

45. 2.505, 20.33, 23, 23.30

46. $\frac{9}{6}, 1.52, 1\frac{4}{7}, 2$

47. $2\frac{8}{9}, 2.95, 3, \frac{19}{6}$

Extensions

48. a.

Date	Transaction	Balance
December 1		$595.50
December 5	Writes a check for $19.95	$575.55
December 12	Writes a check for $280.88	$294.67
December 15	Deposits $257.00	$551.67
December 17	Writes a check for $58.12	$493.55
December 21	Withdraws $50.00	$443.55
December 24	Writes checks for $17.50, $41.37, and $65.15	$319.53
December 26	Deposits $100.00	$419.53
December 31	Withdraws $50.00	$369.53

Figure 7

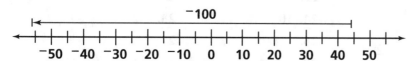

b. $369.53

c. December 1, 2, 3, and 4 ($595.50); however, if the starting balance is excluded, then Kenji had the greatest balance during the month on December 5–11, with $575.55.

d. December 12, 13, and 14 with $294.67

49. 2.5°C; $(20 + {}^-15) \div 2 = 5 \div 2 = 2.5$

50. High was 18°C; $5 = (X + {}^-8) \div 2$; $10 = X + {}^-8$; $18 = X$

51. $^-12.5$°C; $({}^-10 + {}^-15) \div 2 = {}^-12.5$

52–54. Answers will vary.

52. $A = 5, B = 6, 5 + {}^-6 = {}^-1$

53. $A = 2, B = 2, {}^-2 + 2 = 0$

54. $A = 7, B = 5, {}^-7 - {}^-5 = {}^-2$

Possible Answers to Mathematical Reflections

1. a. The number with the greater value (further to the right on the number line) is greater.

  b. The greater the value of the number when its sign is ignored, the less the number (the further to the left on the number line).

  c. A positive number is always greater than a negative number. The positive number is greater than or to the right of zero, and the negative number is less than or to the left of zero.

2. When comparing two numbers, the number further to the right on a horizontal number line, or further up on a vertical number line, is greater.

Mathematical and Problem-Solving Goals

- Develop and use algorithms for adding and subtracting integers

- Model addition and subtraction of integers using distance/direction on a number line and a chip model

- Observe that the Commutative Property holds for addition of rational numbers but not for subtraction of rational numbers

- Understand and use the relationship between addition and subtraction to simplify computation

- Recognize and solve problems involving addition and subtraction of integers

- Solve simple equations with missing facts by using related fact families

- Extend graphing with positive and negative coordinates to all four quadrants

Summary of Problems

Problem 2.1   **Introducing Addition of Integers**

Students use the set model and the number line model to generalize strategies for adding integers.

Problem 2.2   **Introducing Subtraction of Integers**

Students use the set model (chip model) and the number line model to generalize strategies for subtracting integers.

Problem 2.3   **The " + / – " Connection**

Students explore the inverse relationship between addition and subtraction with integers. They formalize the algorithm $a - (-b) = a + b$ and $a - b = a + (-b)$.

Problem 2.4   **Fact Families**

Students use fact families to explore addition and subtraction with integers. They solve equations for missing parts in addition and subtraction problems.

Problem 2.5   **Coordinate Graphing**

This problem extends graphing to all four quadrants using integers.

	Suggested Pacing	Materials for Students	Materials for Teachers	ACE Assignments
All	6 days	Student notebooks	Blank transparencies and transparency markers	
2.1	1 day	Number Lines labsheet, chips or tiles in two colors	Transparencies 2.1A, 2.1B, Number Lines transparency, chips or tiles in two colors	1–3, 30, 37
2.2	$1\frac{1}{2}$ days	Number Lines labsheet, chips or tiles in two colors	Transparencies 2.2A–C, Number Lines transparency, chips or tiles in two colors	4–9, 31, 32, 38, 39
2.3	1 day	Number Lines labsheet, chips or tiles in two colors	Transparency 2.3, chips or tiles in two colors	10–16, 33, 40
2.4	1 day			17–26, 41
2.5	1 day	Labsheet 2.5, Coordinate Grid labsheet, rulers or straightedges	Transparency 2.5, Transparency of number lines (optional) and coordinate grids	27–29, 34–36, 42
MR	$\frac{1}{2}$ day			

2.1 Introducing Addition of Integers

Goals

- Develop algorithms for adding integers
- Model addition of integers using distance/direction on a number line and a chip model
- Observe that the Commutative Property holds for addition of rational numbers

This investigation asks students to clarify their understanding of what it means to add two integers.

Launch 2.1

Models help students make sense of operations like addition with integers. In this problem, we go beyond models to write algorithms for addition. Models provide ways to check students' thinking.

By now, students should be comfortable with using addition in the context of chips (set model) or number line. Show the first problem on an overhead or on the board, separate from the text.

John has 8 video games and his friend has 5. Together they have 8 + 5 = 13 games.

Suggested Question

- *How could you model this problem using chips?* (Answer shown in the Student Edition.)

This is a simple problem for the students. However, your goal in discussing it is to focus on the actions of the problem and how chips can be used to model these actions to get a solution. This helps emphasize the kind of problem for which chips are useful.

Other problems lend themselves to using the directed distance ideas associated with the number line model. Show the second problem on an overhead or on the board, separate from the text.

At a desert weather station, the temperature at sunrise was 10°C. It rose 25°C by noon. The temperature at noon was 10°C + 25°C = 35°C.

Suggested Questions

- *How could you use a number line to model this problem?* (Answer shown in the Student Edition.)

Have students talk through using a number line (make sketches) to show the solution to this problem.

- *How is this problem different from the one before?* (In the first example, you were putting things together or combining. Here, you are adding on to what you already have.)
- *The groups in Question A of Problem 2.1 have something in common that will help you develop an algorithm for addition with integers. Find the sums for a group and think about what the problems have in common.*

Have students work with partners on all parts of the problem.

Explore 2.1

Suggest that they use what they know about working with chips and the number line to help them reason about solving the different problems.

If pairs struggle, have two pairs form a group of four to discuss the problems.

Suggested Question To help students generalize their thinking, ask:

- *How do you know if the solution will be positive or negative?*

Summarize 2.1

Have different teams of students present their solutions to Question A.

Suggested Questions

- *How do you compute problems in which both signs are the same? The signs of the numbers are different?*

When appropriate, have students make up stories for the problems so that their solutions can be tied back to a context.

Discuss the similarities and differences between the problems in each group in Question A to help students formulate an algorithm.

- *For what types of problems did you get a negative number?* (when I added two negatives, or when I added a positive to a negative that was further to the left of zero than the positive addend was to the right of zero)

For Question A, part (3), post several different problems that students have made. For Question B, have students post several problems that give a solution for each number. Writing their solutions as mathematical sentences will help students' understanding of equality that is needed for further work.

- *How can you make a sum that results in exactly $^-5$?* (For the result of $^-5$, one general strategy is to choose two negative addends with numerical values without regard to sign that add to 5. For example, $^-2 + {}^-3 = {}^-5$ and $^-4 + {}^-1 = {}^-5$. Another strategy is to make one addend positive and the other negative, but choose the negative number so that without regard to sign it is 5 greater than the other. For example, $^-10 + {}^+5 = {}^-5$ and $^+25 + {}^-30 = {}^-5$. Or you can think of it as choosing a negative number that is 5 further from zero than the positive addend.)

For Question C, have students share stories for the problems.

- *Which model can represent (a given story): the chip model or the number line model?*
- *Why do you think this?* (Answers will vary. Let students use either model depending on the context of the story.)

Question D explores the Commutative Property to see whether it holds for addition with negative numbers. It does. In the next problem, students explore whether subtraction with negative numbers is commutative. The Commutative Property seems obvious to many students because of their whole-number experience. However, it is important to examine cases where the property does not work, such as subtraction.

Going Further

Compute the following.

$$^-5 + {}^+7 + {}^-14 + {}^-9 = \blacksquare \quad (^-21)$$

2.1 Introducing Addition of Integers

PACING 1 day

Mathematical Goals

- Develop algorithms for adding integers
- Model addition of integers using distance/direction on a number line and a chip model
- Observe that the Commutative Property holds for addition of rational numbers

Launch

Show the first problem on an overhead, separate from the text.

- *How could you model this problem using chips?*

Focus on the actions of the problem and how chips can model these actions.

Show the second problem, separate from the text.

- *How could you use a number line to model this problem?*

Have students talk through using a number line (make sketches) to show the solution.

- *How is this problem different from the one before?*

Have students work with partners.

Materials
- Transparencies 2.1A, 2.1B
- Transparency markers

Explore

Suggest they use what they know about working with chips and the number line to help them reason about the problems.

To help students generalize, ask:

- *How do you know if the solution will be positive or negative?*

Materials
- Number Lines labsheet
- Chips or tiles in two colors

Vocabulary
- Commutative Property

Summarize

Have different teams present their solutions to Question A.

- *How do you compute problems in which both signs are the same? The signs of the numbers are different?*

When appropriate, have students make up stories for the problems so that their solutions can be tied back to a context.

Discuss similarities between problems to help students to a general algorithm.

- *For what types of problems did you get a negative number?*

For Question A, part (3), post several problems that students have made.

Materials
- Student notebooks
- Chip Boards transparency
- Chips or tiles in two colors
- Number Lines transparency

continued on next page

Summarize
continued

For Question B, have students post several possibilities. Writing mathematical sentences will help their understanding of equality needed for further work.

- *How can you make a sum that results in exactly $^-5$?*

For Question C, have students share stories for the problems.

- *Which model—chip or number line—can represent (a given story)?*

Question D explores the Commutative Property to see whether it holds for addition with negative numbers. It does.

Going Further

Compute the following.
$$^-5 + {}^+7 + {}^-14 + {}^-9 = \blacksquare$$

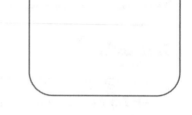

ACE Assignment Guide for Problem 2.1

Differentiated Instruction
Solutions for All Learners

Core 1, 2
Other *Applications* 3, *Connections* 30, *Extensions* 37

Adapted For suggestions about adapting ACE exercises, see the CMP *Special Needs Handbook*.

Answers to Problem 2.1

A. 1.

Group 1
$^+2 + {}^+8 = 10$
$^-3 + {}^-8 = {}^-11$
$^+20 + {}^+25 = 45$
$^-24 + {}^-12 = {}^-36$

Group 2
$^+8 + {}^-12 = {}^-4$
$^-3 + {}^+2 = {}^-1$
$^+14 + {}^-23 = {}^-9$
$^-11 + {}^+13 = 2$

2. Group 1 has addition problems in which the addends have the same sign. Group 2 has addition problems in which the addends have different signs.

3. Answers may vary. Possible answers:
Group 1: $^+6 + {}^+7 = 13$; $^-9 + {}^-5 = {}^-14$;
Group 2: $^+6 + {}^-7 = {}^-1$; $^-9 + {}^+5 = {}^-4$

4. For problems in Group 1, add the values without the signs (absolute values) of the two numbers. Give the sign of the addends to the sum. For problems in Group 2, find

the difference of the numbers without signs (absolute values). The sign of the number with the greatest absolute value is the sign of the sum.

B. Answers will vary. Possible answers:

1. $^-3 + {}^-2 = {}^-5$, $^-10 + {}^+5 = {}^-5$, $^-14 + {}^+9 = {}^-5$

2. $^+7 + {}^+8 = {}^+15$, $^+21 + {}^-6 = {}^+15$, $^-15 + {}^+30 = {}^+15$

3. $^+7 + {}^-7 = 0$, $^+21 + {}^-21 = 0$, $^-15 + {}^+15 = 0$

4. a. $^+8$ **b.** $^-2\frac{1}{4}$ **c.** $^-1\frac{1}{4}$

C. 1–3. Answers will vary. Possible answers given.

1. After receiving a check for $50 and writing a check for $65, what change did Bill have in his account?

2. The evening temperature registered $^-15°F$. By midnight, the temperature was $^-25°F$. What was the change in temperature?

3. Sally has expenses of $300 and $250. How much does she owe altogether?

D. 1. Both expressions equal $^-23$.

2. Both expressions equal $^-8\frac{5}{6}$.

3. It does not matter in which order the addends are written. The sum is the same.

2.2 Introducing Subtraction of Integers

Goals

- Develop algorithms for subtracting integers

- Model subtraction of integers using distance/direction on a number line and a chip model

- Observe that the Commutative Property does not hold for subtraction of rational numbers

This investigation asks students to clarify their understanding of what it means to subtract two integers.

Launch 2.2

By now, students should be comfortable with using addition in the context of chips (set model) or number line. Show Example 1 on an overhead or on the board, separate from the text.

Kim had 9 CDs. She sold 4 CDs at a yard sale. She now has only 9 − 4 = 5 of those CDs left.

This is a simple and obvious problem for the students. However, your goal in discussing it is to focus on the actions of the problem and how chips can be used to model these actions to get a solution. This helps emphasize the kind of problem for which chips are useful.

The second situation, $^+5 - {}^+7$, is more complex. In this situation, students need to think about a way to represent $^+5$ so that $^+7$ can be removed. This means showing $^+5$ as some combination of black and red chips. Be sure to model the actions of this problem with students, making sure that you write mathematical sentences that reflect the changes made to the board. When you rename 5 on the board, rename 5 in the expression, $^-2 + {}^+2 + {}^+5 - 7$ or $^-2 + {}^+7 - 7$. You may want to model a few other problems as well (e.g., $^-7 - {}^+2$ and so on) so students can become comfortable with different ways to show an integer quantity using chips.

Other problems lend themselves to using the directed distance ideas associated with the number line model. Show the second problem on an overhead or on the board, separate from the text.

Suggested Question

- *The Arroyo family just passed mile 25 on the highway. They need to get to the exit at mile 80. How many more miles do they have to drive?* (They still have to drive 80 − 25 = 55 miles.)

Have students talk through using a number line (make sketches) to show the solution to this problem.

Discuss that the measure of distance is always positive. The sign of the answer tells you direction. A result of $^-82$ would mean a distance of 82 in a negative direction. If you have not discussed absolute value earlier, do so here. Then you can characterize the distance as the absolute value and the sign as the direction.

While models help students make sense of operations like subtraction with integers, they are ready to move toward a more abstract stage in their understandings.

Have students start Question A individually and then move to small groups to discuss their findings.

Explore 2.2

Suggest that they use what they know about working with chips and the number line to help them reason about solving the different problems in the two groups.

Once students make sense of Question A, have them move on to Questions B and C.

Summarize 2.2

Have different teams of students present their solutions to Question A.

Suggested Question

- *How do you compute problems in which both signs are the same? The signs of the numbers are different?*

When appropriate, have students make up stories for the problems so that their solutions can be tied back to a context.

Discuss the similarities and differences between problems in a group.

- *How do you know if the difference is positive or negative?* (When you are subtracting, you will get a positive answer if the number you start with is greater than the number you subtract. For example, $^+17 - {}^+15$, $17 - {}^-1$, and $^-15 - {}^-21$ give positive results. You will get a negative result if the number you start with is less than the number you subtract. For example, $^+13 - {}^+15$, $^-1 - {}^+15$, and $^-15 - {}^-13$ give negative results.)

- *When you are subtracting with integers, must you always think of the operation as subtraction? Why or why not?* (No. You can change a subtraction to an "add the opposite" problem.)

For Question B, post several different problems that students have made. Organizing their work into categories (both positive numbers, both negative numbers, or one positive and one negative) may help facilitate the discussion. Discuss ways in which problems can be structured to produce the solutions requested. For example, for the result of $^-5$, one general strategy is to make the number you start with negative and the number you subtract negative but with an absolute value of five less than the absolute value of the number you start with so that the difference will be $^-5$; ($^-15 - {}^-10$). Another strategy is to make both numbers positive, with the number you subtract greater than the number you start with by 5; ($^+23 - {}^+28$).

For Question C, have students focus on the Commutative Property. Looking back at the

introduction to the problem, they can see that addition is commutative. However, as they experiment with subtraction examples, they will see that this property does not extend to subtraction. A number line representation can help students "see" the property, and that it is not valid for subtraction.

$$^-2 - {}^+3 = {}^-5 \qquad\qquad {}^+3 - {}^-2 = {}^+5$$

$$^-5 \ {}^-4 \ {}^-3 \ {}^-2 \ {}^-1 \ 0 \ {}^+1 \ {}^+2 \ {}^+3 \ {}^+4 \ {}^+5$$

These are not the same.

Check for Understanding

- *Without computing the answers, predict how the answers to the following two computations in each pair will compare. Will the answers be the same or different? If they are different, which will be greater? Explain.*

  1. $^-7 + {}^-8$ and $^-7 - {}^+8$

  2. $^-12 - {}^-4$ and $^-4 - {}^-12$

(In the first pair, the answers are both -15. Adding $^-8$ gives the same result as subtracting 8. In the second pair, subtraction is not commutative. The answer to the second part will be greater than the first because you add 12 in the second and only 4 in the first. The answer to the first part is $^-8$ and the second part is $^+8$.)

2.2 Introducing Subtraction of Integers

Mathematical Goals

- Develop algorithms for subtracting integers
- Model subtraction using distance/direction on a number line and a chip model
- Observe that the Commutative Property does not hold for subtraction of rational numbers

Launch

Show the first problem on an overhead, separate from the text. Focus on the actions of the problem and how chips can be used to model these actions. In the second situation, students need to represent $^+5$ so that $^+7$ can be removed. Model the actions and write mathematical sentences that reflect the changes made. You may want to model a few other problems as well.

Show the second problem, separate from the text. Have students show the solution using a number line (make sketches). Discuss that the measure of distance is always positive. The sign of the answer tells you direction.

Have students start Question A individually and then move to small groups to discuss their findings.

Materials
- Transparencies 2.2A, 2.2B, 2.2C
- Transparency markers

Vocabulary
- absolute value

Explore

Suggest students use what they know about working with chips and the number line to help them reason about the problems in the two groups.

Once students make sense of Question A, move on to Questions B and C.

Materials
- Chips or tiles in two colors
- Number Lines labsheet

Summarize

Have different teams present their solutions to Question A.

- *How do you compute problems in which both signs are the same? The signs of the numbers are different?*

When appropriate, have students make up stories for the problems so that their solutions can be tied back to a context.

Discuss similarities between problems to help students to a general algorithm.

- *How do you know if the difference is positive or negative?*
- *When you are subtracting with integers, must you always think of the operation as subtraction? Why or why not?*

For Question B, post and organize several problems that students have made (categories: both positive numbers, both negative numbers, or one positive and one negative). Discuss ways problems can be structured to produce the solutions.

For Question C, have students focus on the Commutative Property.

Materials
- Student notebooks
- Number Lines transparency
- Chip Boards transparency
- Chips or tiles in two colors
- Small Chip Boards labsheet

continued on next page

Check for Understanding

- *Without computing the answers, predict how the answers in each pair will compare. Will the answers be the same or different? If they are different, which will be greater? Explain.*

    1. $^-7 + ^-8$ and $^-7 - ^+8$ **2.** $^-12 - ^-4$ and $^-4 - ^-12$

ACE Assignment Guide for Problem 2.2

Core 6, 7

Other *Applications* 4, 5, 8, 9; *Connections* 31, 32, *Extensions* 38, 39; unassigned choices from previous problems

Adapted For suggestions about adapting Exercise 4 and other ACE exercises, see the CMP *Special Needs Handbook*.

Answers to Problem 2.2

A. 1.

Group 1	Group 2
$^+12 - ^+8 = ^+4$	$^+12 - ^-8 = ^+20$
$^-5 - ^-7 = ^+2$	$^-5 - ^+7 = ^-12$
$^-4 - ^-2 = ^-2$	$^-4 - ^+2 = ^-6$
$^+2 - ^+4 = ^-2$	$^+2 - ^-4 = ^+6$

2. In Group 1, the signs of numbers are the same, and in Group 2, the signs of numbers are different.

3. Answers may vary. Possible answers:
Group 1: $^+9 - ^+7 = ^+2$; $^-11 - ^-8 = ^-3$;
Group 2: $^+1 - ^-7 = ^+8$; $^-10 - ^+8 = ^-18$

4. There are various strategies that may surface.

Students may already see that you can change the subtraction to an addition by adding the opposite.

Some may realize that when you are subtracting, you will get a positive answer if the number you start with is greater than the number you subtract. For example, $^+17 - ^+15$, $^+17 - ^-1$, and $^-15 - ^-21$ give positive results. You will get a negative result if the number you start with is less than the number you subtract. For example, $^+13 - ^+15$, $^-1 - ^+15$, and $^-15 - ^-13$ give negative results. To find the value of

the answer, you find the difference of the numbers.

If you have talked about absolute value and your students understand, they may give the following:

For problems in Group 1, find the difference of the absolute values of the two numbers. If the first number is greater than the second number, the difference will be positive. If the first number is less than the second number, the difference will be negative.

For problems in Group 2, find the sum of the absolute values of the two numbers. The sign of the answer will be the sign of the first number.

Some students will want to think in terms of four sub-categories.

Pos $-$ Pos: Positive if number you start with is greater than number you subtract and negative otherwise.

Pos $-$ Neg: Positive

Neg $-$ Neg: Positive if number you start with is greater than number you subtract and negative otherwise.

Neg $-$ Pos: Negative

5. a. $^-4$ **b.** $^-1\frac{3}{4}$ **c.** $^+\frac{1}{2}$ **d.** $^-\frac{3}{4}$

B. Answers will vary. Possible answers:

1. $^-3 - ^+2 = ^-5$, $^-10 - ^-5 = ^-5$, $^-14 - ^-9 = ^-5$

2. $^+7 - ^-8 = ^+15$, $^+21 - ^+6 = ^+15$, $^-15 - ^-30 = ^+15$

3. $^-7 - ^-7 = 0$, $^-21 - ^-21 = 0$, $^+15 - ^+15 = 0$

4. $^-7 - ^-3.5 = ^-3.5$, $0 - ^+3.5 = ^-3.5$, $^+7.5 - ^+11 = ^-3.5$

C. No, for all four examples. Subtraction is not commutative. Encourage students to experiment with different examples.

2.3 The "+/−" Connection

Goals

- Understand and use the relationship between addition and subtraction to simplify computation by changing subtraction problems to addition or vice versa

- Use algorithms for adding and subtracting integers

- Recognize and solve problems involving addition and subtraction of integers

Launch 2.3

Use the Getting Ready to engage students with the chip-board diagram and the sentences to be completed. This is designed to help students build the "+/−" connection. Through trials, they should recognize that restating subtraction of a positive as addition of a negative or restating subtraction of a negative as addition of a positive produces the same results and can simplify calculations.

1. $^+5 + {}^-3 = {}^+2$ (add 3 red chips to the board)
   $^+5 - {}^+3 = {}^+2$ (remove 3 black chips from the board)

2. $^+5 + {}^+3 = {}^+8$ (add 3 black chips to the board)
   $^+5 - {}^-3 = ({}^+5 + {}^+3 + {}^-3) - {}^-3 =$
   $^+8 + {}^-3 - {}^-3 = {}^+8$ (represent $^+5$ as
   $^+8 + {}^-3$ by adding 3 red chips and 3 black chips to the board; remove 3 red chips from the board)

The problem engages students further in observing and using these relationships. At this point, students may have some conjectures about general relationships.

Let students work alone for a while and then discuss their work with a partner or small group.

Explore 2.3

Some students may think of the equal sign (=) as "it tells me to do something," not as "it says two things are equivalent." As you listen to their conversations, ask them to think about what it means to restate a problem in an "equivalent form." Also remind them that they can model the problem with the chip-board model or a number-line model to try out their ideas.

Summarize 2.3

Have teams share their results to the problems.

In looking for general relationships, it may be easier to look at subtraction and see what needs to be done to find a related addition problem (i.e., add the opposite of what is being subtracted). A similar relationship exists for addition (i.e., subtract the opposite of what is being added).

Suggested Questions

- *What do you know about the relationship between addition and subtraction for integers?* (You can change a subtraction problem to adding the opposite and you can change an addition problem to subtracting the opposite. Either way you get equivalent amounts.)

- *How can this help in stating an algorithm for subtracting any integer?* (You really only need to know an algorithm for addition. Every subtraction problem can be changed to addition. So, our subtraction algorithm can be: Instead of subtracting, add the opposite.)

2.3 The "+/−" Connection

Mathematical Goals

- Understand and use the relationship between addition and subtraction to simplify computation by changing subtraction problems to addition or vice versa
- Use algorithms for adding and subtracting integers
- Recognize and solve problems involving addition and subtraction of integers

Launch

Use the Getting Ready to engage students with the chip-board diagram and the sentences to be completed. This is designed to help students build the "+/−" connection.

1. $^+5 + {}^-3 = {}^+2$ (add 3 red chips to the board)

   $^+5 - {}^+3 = {}^+2$ (remove 3 black chips from the board)

2. $^+5 + {}^+3 = {}^+8$ (add 3 black chips to the board)

   $^+5 - {}^-3 = ({}^+5 + {}^+3 + {}^-3) - {}^-3 = {}^+8 + {}^-3 - {}^-3 = {}^+8$

   (represent $^+5$ as $^+8 + {}^-3$ by adding 3 red chips and 3 black chips to the board; remove 3 red chips from the board)

Use a Think-Pair-Share arrangement for this problem.

Materials
- Transparency 2.3
- Transparency markers
- Chips or tiles in two colors

Explore

Some students may think of the equal sign (=) as "it tells me to do something," not as "it says two things are equivalent." As you listen to their conversations, ask them to think about what it means to restate a problem in an "equivalent form." Remind them that they can model the problem with the chip-board model or a number-line model to try out their ideas.

Materials
- Number Lines labsheet
- Chips or tiles in two colors
- Small Chip Boards labsheet

Summarize

Have teams share their results to the problems.

In looking for general relationships, it may be easier to look at subtraction and see what needs to be done to find a related addition problem (i.e., add the opposite of what is being subtracted). A similar relationship exists for addition (i.e., subtract the opposite of what is being added).

- *What do you know about the relationship between addition and subtraction for integers?*
- *How can this help in stating an algorithm for subtracting any integer?*

Materials
- Student notebooks

ACE Assignment Guide
for Problem 2.3

Core 10, 11
Other *Applications* 12–16, *Connections* 33,
Extensions 40; unassigned choices from previous
problems

Adapted For suggestions about adapting ACE
exercises, see the CMP *Special Needs Handbook*.
Connecting to Prior Units 33: *Bits and Pieces I*

Answers to Problem 2.3

A. 1. $^+5 + {}^-2 = {}^+5 - {}^+2$

2. $^+5 + {}^+4 = {}^+5 - {}^-4$

3. $^-7 + {}^-2 = {}^-7 - {}^+2$

4. $^-7 + {}^+2 = {}^-7 - {}^-2$

B. Any addition problem can be written as a
subtraction problem. For example,
$^+5 + {}^-2 = {}^+5 - {}^+2$ and $^+5 + {}^+2 =$
$^+5 - {}^-2$. You can demonstrate this
equivalence, $^+5 + {}^-2 = {}^+5 - {}^+2$, on a chip
board by starting with 5 black chips and
adding 2 red chips to get a value of 3. Or start
with 5 black chips and remove 2 of them to
end up with 3 black chips.

C. 1. $^+8 - {}^+5 = {}^+8 + {}^-5$

2. $^+8 - {}^-5 = {}^+8 + {}^+5$

3. $^-4 - {}^+6 = {}^-4 + {}^-6$

4. $^-4 - {}^-6 = {}^-4 + {}^+6$

D. Any subtraction problem can be written as an
addition problem. For example,
$^+8 - {}^+5 = {}^+8 + {}^-5$. To illustrate this on a
chip board, start with 8 black chips and
remove 5 of them to end up with 3 black
chips. Or start with 8 black chips and add
5 red chips to get a value of 3.

E. 1. $^+396 + {}^+400 = {}^+796$

2. $^-75.8 + {}^+35.2 = {}^-40.6$

3. $^-25.6 - {}^+4.4 = {}^-30$

4. $^+\frac{3}{2} + {}^-\frac{1}{4} = {}^+\frac{5}{4}$

5. $^+\frac{5}{8} - {}^+\frac{3}{4} = {}^-\frac{1}{8}$

6. $^-3\frac{1}{2} + {}^-5 = {}^-\frac{17}{2}$ or $^-8\frac{1}{2}$

2.4 Fact Families

Goals

- Understand and use the relationship between addition and subtraction found in fact families
- Solve simple equations with missing facts by using related fact families

Launch 2.4

Review with students what they know about fact families. Fact families were introduced in grade 6 in the number units. Make sure your students understand that fact families are built based on the relationship between addition and subtraction. If you think your students will need the help, develop a fact family with them like the following:

$$3 + 2 = 5 \qquad 2 + 3 = 5$$
$$5 - 3 = 2 \qquad 5 - 2 = 3$$

Suggested Question

- *Look carefully at the relationships in the fact family. Why are these relationships true?* (The two addition sentences are true because addition is commutative. The two subtraction sentences are true because either addend can be found by subtracting the other addend from the sum, 5.)

Have students work individually on Questions A and B. Then have them work with a partner to discuss their ideas and complete the problem.

Explore 2.4

Ask for explanations as you circulate. If a student or pair is struggling, you might want to observe and ask questions to get a fact family with negative numbers. Here is an example:

$$^-7 + {}^+2 = {}^-5 \qquad {}^+2 + {}^-7 = {}^-5$$
$$^-5 - {}^+2 = {}^-7 \qquad {}^-5 - {}^-7 = {}^+2$$

Students need to see that these ideas are just extensions of what they already know from whole numbers.

Question D may be difficult for some students. If they are thrown off by the variable, n, suggest that they replace it with a question mark and say in words what they are trying to find. If they are still confused, substitute 39 for n, write the fact family, and then rewrite it with n in the place of 39.

Summarize 2.4

Have teams share their results to the problems. Highlight Questions C and D, asking students how they might use what they know about fact families to solve for an unknown number in addition and subtraction sentences. Look back at Problems 2.1 and 2.2 and choose a few parts from Question A in each. Have students discuss how they might restate the problem using what they know about fact families and solve the problem.

Going Further

1. If $^-n = {}^+8$, what does n equal? ($^-8$)
2. If $^-n = {}^-8$, what does n equal? ($^+8$)
3. Write a related fact for $^-4 + {}^-n = {}^+10$ that makes it easy to find the value for n. ($^+10 - {}^-4 = {}^-n$ gives the opposite of n which is 14, so $n = {}^-14$.)

2.4 Fact Families

Mathematical Goals

- Understand and use the relationship between addition and subtraction found in fact families
- Solve simple equations with missing facts by using related fact families

Launch

Review with students what they know about fact families. Make sure students understand that fact families are built based on the relationship between addition and subtraction. If your students need the help, develop a fact family with them like the following:

$$3 + 2 = 5 \qquad 2 + 3 = 5 \qquad 5 - 3 = 2 \qquad 5 - 2 = 3$$

- *Why are these relationships true?*

The two addition sentences are true because addition is commutative. The two subtraction sentences are true because either addend can be found by subtracting the other addend from the sum, 5.

Have students work individually on Questions A and B. Then have them work with a partner to discuss their ideas and complete the problem.

Materials
- Transparency markers

Explore

Ask for explanations as you circulate. If a student or pair is struggling, observe and ask questions to get a fact family with negative numbers.

Students need to see that these ideas are just extensions of what they already know from whole numbers.

Question D may be difficult for some students. If they are thrown off by the variable, n, suggest they replace it with a question mark and say in words what they are trying to find. If they are still confused, substitute 39 for n, write the fact family, and then rewrite it with n in the place of 39.

Summarize

Have teams share their results to the problems.

Highlight Questions C and D, asking students how they might use what they know about fact families to solve for an unknown number in addition and subtraction sentences.

Look back at Problems 2.1 and 2.2 and choose a few parts from Question A in each. Have students discuss how they might restate the problem using what they know about fact families and solve the problem.

Materials
- Student notebooks

continued on next page

Summarize

continued

Going Further

1. If $^-n = {}^+8$, what does n equal?

2. If $^-n = {}^-8$, what does n equal?

3. Write a related fact for $^-4 + {}^-n = {}^+10$ that makes it easy to find the value for n.

ACE Assignment Guide for Problem 2.4

Core 17–22, 24–26
Other *Connections* 23, *Extensions* 41; unassigned choices from previous problems

Adapted For suggestions about adapting ACE exercises, see the CMP *Special Needs Handbook*.

Answers to Problem 2.4

A. 1. $^-5 - {}^-3 = {}^-2$ or $^-5 - {}^-2 = {}^-3$

2. $^-7 - {}^-32 = {}^+25$ or $^-7 - 25 = {}^-32$

B. 1. $^+10 + {}^-2 = {}^+8$ or $^-2 + {}^+10 = {}^+8$

2. $^+6 + {}^-20 = {}^-14$ or $^-20 + {}^+6 = {}^-14$

C. 1. a. $n - {}^+35 = {}^+5; n = {}^+35 + {}^+5$ or $^+35 + {}^+5 = n.$

b. $n - {}^+35 = {}^-5; n = {}^+35 + {}^-5$ or $^-5 + {}^+35 = n.$

c. $n - {}^+35 = {}^-5; n = {}^-5 + {}^+35$ or $^+35 + {}^-5 = n.$

2. Possible answer: Yes, it is easier to think about addition.

D. 1. a. $^+43 - n = {}^+4$ or $^+43 - {}^+4 = n$

b. $^+43 - n = {}^-4$ or $^+43 - {}^-4 = n$ or $^+43 + {}^+4 = n$

c. $^-43 - n = {}^-4$ or $^-43 - {}^-4 = n$ or $^-43 + {}^+4 = n$

2. Students often find the "missing addend" problem to be easier to reason about. For example, $^-4 + n = {}^+43$. Other students may find one of the other forms easier, like $^+43 + {}^+4 = n.$

2.5 Coordinate Graphing

Goal

- Extend graphing with positive and negative coordinates to all four quadrants

In previous units, students have graphed in the first quadrant of a coordinate grid. Their work with integers now facilitates the introduction of the complete coordinate grid. You may want to refer to work done in the *Variables and Patterns* and *Stretching and Shrinking* units to help students remember where they have used coordinate grids before.

Launch 2.5

Introduce the situation. Help students see that the axes for the four-quadrant grid are made by crossing two perpendicular number lines at the (0, 0) point. You can demonstrate this to students by showing a horizontal number line and then overlaying a vertical number line. With the class, examine a coordinate grid and label the tick marks on the two axes. Spend a few minutes looking at how the grid is made, and challenge the class to locate the point ($^-3$, $^+5$) and a few others. This should get students thinking about the ramification of now having four quadrants in which to locate points.

When students have an idea of how to locate points on the grid, let them work in pairs on the problem.

Students should be encouraged to read coordinate pairs correctly. For example ($^-3$, $^+5$) is read "negative 3, positive 5." Some students want to insert the word "and" between the numbers.

Explore 2.5

Circulate to make sure students understand how to locate points.

Suggested Questions Ask students to tell which quadrant a particular point is in and vice versa.

- *What are the signs of coordinates of a point that will fall in Quadrant III? $(-, -)$ What about Quadrant IV? $(+, -)$ Quadrant II? $(-, +)$*

Summarize 2.5

For each part of the problem, call on more than one pair of students to share their solution. A good way to share solutions is to have students plot points on a transparent coordinate grid.

Suggested Questions

- *How do you know the quadrant in which a point will fall?*

- *Why will a point (x, y) with both values negative fall in Quadrant III?*

- *What do you notice about the line segment that connects a point to its opposite point?* (It goes through the origin. The opposite point for a point in Quadrant I lies in Quadrant III. For points in Quadrant II, the opposite lies in Quadrant IV.)

Going Further
Start with the point ($^+1$, $^-1$). Plot the point that you get by multiplying each of the coordinates by $^-2$. Then multiply the resulting coordinates by $^-2$ and plot that point. Continue until you plot four points.

- *What patterns do you see in the points that you get?* (They lie on a straight line and alternate between Quadrant IV and Quadrant II.)

2.5 Coordinate Graphing

Mathematical Goal

- Extend graphing with positive and negative coordinates to all four quadrants

Launch

Introduce the situation. Help students see that the axes for the four-quadrant grid are made by crossing two perpendicular number lines at the (0, 0) point. Show a horizontal number line and then overlaying a vertical number line.

With the class, examine a coordinate grid and label the tick marks on the two axes. Spend a few minutes looking at how the grid is made, and challenge the class to locate the point ($^-3$, $^+5$) and a few others. This should get students thinking about the ramification of now having four quadrants in which to locate points.

When students have an idea of how to locate points on the grid, let them work in pairs on the problem.

Materials
- Number Lines transparency
- Transparency 2.5
- Transparency markers

Vocabulary
- Quadrant I, II, III, IV

Explore

Circulate to make sure students understand how to locate points. Ask students to tell which quadrant a particular point is in and vice versa.

- *What are the signs of coordinates of a point that will fall in Quadrant III? What about Quadrant IV? Quadrant II?*

Materials
- Labsheet 2.5
- Rulers or straightedges

Summarize

For each part of the problem, call on more than one pair of students to share their solution. A good way to share solutions is to have students plot points on a transparent coordinate grid.

- *How do you know the quadrant in which a point will fall?*
- *Why will a point (x, y) with both values negative fall in Quadrant III?*
- *What do you notice about the line segment that connects a point to its opposite point?*

Going Further

Start with the point ($^+1$, $^-1$) and plot the point that you get by multiplying each of the coordinates by $^-2$. Then multiply the resulting coordinates by $^-2$ and plot that point. Continue until you plot four points.

- *What patterns do you see in the points that you get?*

Materials
- Student notebooks
- Coordinate Grid transparency and labsheet

ACE Assignment Guide for Problem 2.5

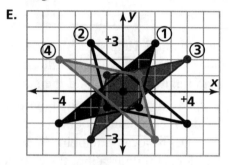

Differentiated Instruction
Solutions for All Learners

Core 27, 34, 42
Other *Applications* 28, 29; *Connections* 35, 36; unassigned choices from previous problems

Adapted For suggestions about adapting ACE exercises, see the CMP *Special Needs Handbook*.
Connecting to Prior Units 34: *Stretching and Shrinking*; 35, 36: *Variables and Patterns*

Answers to Problem 2.5

A. A ($^-$8, $^+$7) B ($^-$2, $^+$6)
   C ($^+$7, $^+$2) D ($^+$9, $^-$7)
   E ($^+$4, $^-$5) F ($^-$4, $^-$2)
   G ($^-$7, $^-$8) H (0, 0)

B. Quadrant I: (+, +)
   Quadrant II: (−, +)
   Quadrant III: (−, −)
   Quadrant IV: (+, −)

Figure 1

Quadrant II   **Quadrant I**

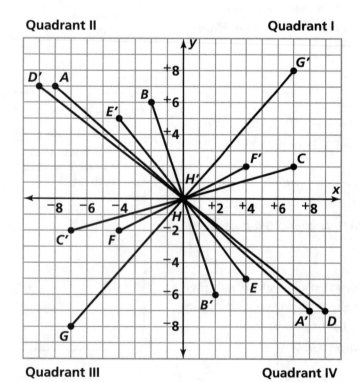

Quadrant III   **Quadrant IV**

C. A′ ($^+$8, $^-$7) B′ ($^+$2, $^-$6)
   C′ ($^-$7, $^-$2) D′ ($^-$9, $^+$7)
   E′ ($^-$4, $^+$5) F′ ($^+$4, $^+$2)
   G′ ($^+$7, $^+$8) H′ (0, 0)
   See Figure 1.

D. (Figure 1) All of the segments go through the origin.

E.

(**Note:** You can transform triangle 4 to triangle 2 by rotating it around the origin. You can do the same with triangles 1 and 3.)

5. Triangle 1 is the same shape and size as triangles 2, 3, and 4. Triangle 2 is triangle 1 reflected (or flipped) over the *y*-axis. Triangle 3 is triangle 1 flipped over the diagonal line *y* = *x*. Triangle 4 is triangle 1 flipped over the *x*-axis.

The student edition pages for this investigation begin on the next page.

Notes _____
_____
_____
_____

Adding and Subtracting Integers

In Investigation 1, you used number lines and chip boards to model operations with integers. Now, you will develop algorithms for adding and subtracting integers.

An **algorithm** is a plan, or series of steps, for doing a computation. In an effective algorithm, the steps lead to the correct answer, no matter what numbers you use. You may even develop more than one algorithm for each computation. Your goal should be to understand and skillfully use at least one algorithm for adding integers and at least one algorithm for subtracting integers.

2.1 Introducing Addition of Integers

There are two common ways that number problems lead to addition calculations like 8 + 5. The first involves combining two similar sets of objects, like in this example:

> John has 8 video games and his friend has 5. Together they have
> 8 + 5 = 13 games.

22 Accentuate the Negative

Notes _____

_____

_____

_____

You can represent this situation on a chip board.

8 + 5 = 13

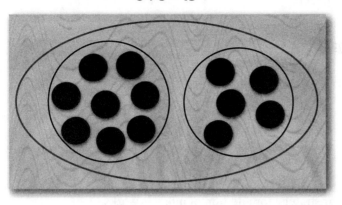

Number problems also lead to addition calculations when you add to a starting number. Take the following example:

At a desert weather station, the temperature at sunrise was 10°C. It rose 25°C by noon. The temperature at noon was 10°C + 25°C = 35°C.

You can represent this situation on a number line. The starting point is $^+10$. The change in distance and direction is $^+25$. The sum ($^+35$) is the result of moving that distance and direction.

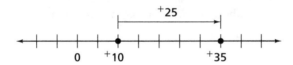

Suppose, instead of rising 25°C, the temperature fell 15°C. The next number line shows that $^+10°C + {}^-15°C = {}^-5°C$.

Use these ideas about addition as you develop an algorithm for addition of integers.

Notes _____

_____

_____

_____

Problem 2.1 Introducing Addition of Integers

Use chip models or number line models.

A. 1. Find the sums in each group.

2. Describe what the examples in each group have in common.

3. Use your answer to part (2) to write two problems for each group.

4. Describe an algorithm for adding integers in each group.

Group 1	Group 2
$^+2 + {}^+8$	$^+8 + {}^-12$
$^-3 + {}^-8$	$^-3 + {}^+2$
$^+20 + {}^+25$	$^+14 + {}^-23$
$^-24 + {}^-12$	$^-11 + {}^+13$

B. Write each number as a sum of integers in three different ways.

1. $^-5$ **2.** $^+15$ **3.** 0

4. Check to see whether your strategy for addition of integers works on these rational number problems.

a. $^-1 + {}^+9$ **b.** $^-1\frac{1}{2} + {}^-\frac{3}{4}$ **c.** $^+1\frac{1}{2} + {}^-2\frac{3}{4}$

C. Write a story to match each number sentence. Find the solutions.

1. $^+50 + {}^-65 = \blacksquare$ **2.** $^-15 + \blacksquare = {}^-25$ **3.** $^-300 + {}^-250 = \blacksquare$

D. Find both sums in parts (1) and (2). What do you notice?

1. $^+12 + {}^-35$ $^-35 + {}^+12$ **2.** $^-7\frac{2}{3} + {}^-1\frac{1}{6}$ $^-1\frac{1}{6} + {}^-7\frac{2}{3}$

3. The property of rational numbers that you have observed is called the **Commutative Property** of addition. What do you think the Commutative Property says about addition of rational numbers?

ACE Homework starts on page 32.

2.2 Introducing Subtraction of Integers

In some subtraction problems, you *take away* objects from a set, as in this first example:

Example 1 Kim had 9 CDs. She sold 4 CDs at a yard sale. She now has only $9 - 4 = 5$ of those CDs left.

Notes _____

_____

_____

_____

$$9 - 4 = 5$$

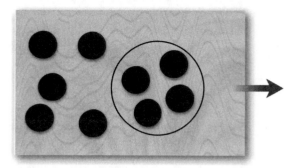

You can represent this situation on a chip board.

Here is another example.

> **Example 2** Otis earned $5 babysitting. He owes Latoya $7. He pays her the $5. Represent this integer subtraction on a chip board.

To subtract 7 from 5 ($^+5 - {^+7}$), start by showing $^+5$ as black chips.

You can't take away $^+7$ because there aren't seven black chips to remove. Since adding both a red chip and a black chip does not change the value of the board, add two black chips and two red chips. The value of the board stays the same, but now there are 7 black chips to take away.

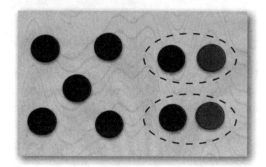

$$5 - 7 = {^-2}$$

What is left on the board when you take away the 7 black chips?

The changes on the board can be represented by $(^-2 + 2) + 5 - 7 = {^-2}$. Otis now has $^-\$2$. He still owes Latoya $2.

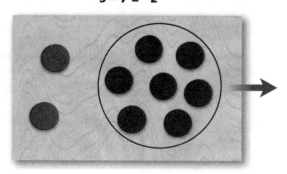

Investigation 2 Adding and Subtracting Integers **25**

STUDENT PAGE

Notes _____

_____

_____

_____

In a third example of a subtraction problem, you find the *difference* between two numbers.

Example 3 The Arroyo family just passed mile 25 on the highway. They need to get to the exit at mile 80. How many more miles do they have to drive?

You can use a number line to show differences.

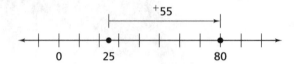

The arrow on the number line points in the direction of travel. The Arroyos are traveling in a positive direction from small values to greater values. They still have to travel 80 − 25 = 55 miles.

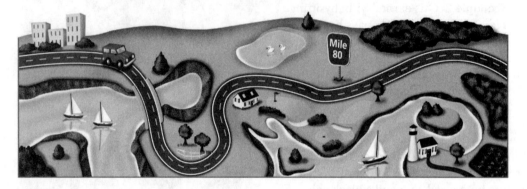

If the Arroyos drive back from mile 80 to mile 25, they still have to travel 55 miles. This time, however, they travel in the opposite direction. The number sentence 25 − 80 = ⁻55 represents this situation.

Now, the arrow points to the left and has a label of ⁻55. The distance is 55, but the direction is negative.

Sometimes you only want the distance and not direction. You can show distance by putting vertical bars around the given number. This is called absolute value. The **absolute value** of a number is its distance from 0 on the number line.

$$|{}^-55| = 55 \qquad |{}^+55| = 55$$

You say "the absolute value of ⁻55 is 55" and "the absolute value of ⁺55 is 55."

26 Accentuate the Negative

Notes _____

_____

_____

_____

When you write a number and a sign (or an implied sign for +) on an arrow above a number line, you are indicating both distance and direction.

In a problem that involves the amount of money you have and the amount that you owe, is the sign (direction) important?

Problem 2.2 Introducing Subtraction of Integers

Use chip models or number line models.

A. 1. Find the differences in each group below.

Group 1	Group 2
$^{+}12 - {}^{+}8$	$^{+}12 - {}^{-}8$
$^{-}5 - {}^{-}7$	$^{-}5 - {}^{+}7$
$^{-}4 - {}^{-}2$	$^{-}4 - {}^{+}2$
$^{+}2 - {}^{+}4$	$^{+}2 - {}^{-}4$

  2. Describe what the examples in each group have in common.

  3. Use your answer to part (2) to write two problems for each group.

  4. Describe an algorithm for subtracting integers in each group.

  5. Check to see whether your strategy for subtraction of integers works on these rational number problems:

  a. $^{-}1 - {}^{+}3$ **b.** $^{-}1 - {}^{+}\frac{3}{4}$

  c. $^{-}1\frac{1}{2} - {}^{-}2$ **d.** $^{-}1\frac{1}{2} - {}^{-}\frac{3}{4}$

B. Write each number as a difference of integers in three different ways.

  1. $^{-}5$ **2.** $^{+}15$

  3. 0   **4.** $^{-}3.5$

C. For parts (1)–(4), decide whether the expressions are equal.

  1. $^{-}2 - {}^{+}3 \stackrel{?}{=} {}^{+}3 - {}^{-}2$ **2.** $^{+}12 - {}^{-}4 \stackrel{?}{=} {}^{-}4 - {}^{+}12$

  3. $^{-}15 - {}^{-}20 \stackrel{?}{=} {}^{-}20 - {}^{-}15$ **4.** $^{+}45 - {}^{+}21 \stackrel{?}{=} {}^{+}21 - {}^{+}45$

  5. Do you think there is a Commutative Property of subtraction?

ACE Homework starts on page 32.

Investigation 2 Adding and Subtracting Integers   **27**

Notes _____

_____

_____

_____

(27) 56

2.3 The "+/−" Connection

You have probably noticed that addition and subtraction are related to each other. You can write any addition sentence as an equivalent subtraction sentence. You can also write any subtraction sentence as an equivalent addition sentence.

Getting Ready for Problem 2.3

The chip board below shows a value of $^+5$.

- There are two possible moves, one addition and one subtraction, that would change the value on the board to $^+2$ in one step. How would you complete the number sentences to represent each move?

$$^+5 + \blacksquare = {}^+2 \text{ and } {}^+5 - \blacksquare = {}^+2$$

- There are two possible moves, one addition and one subtraction, that would change the value on the board to $^+8$ in one step. How would you complete the number sentences to represent each move?

$$^+5 + \blacksquare = {}^+8 \text{ and } {}^+5 - \blacksquare = {}^+8$$

- Can you describe a general relationship between addition and subtraction for integers?

28   Accentuate the Negative

STUDENT PAGE

Notes _____

_____

_____

_____

STUDENT PAGE

Problem 2.3 Addition and Subtraction Relationships

Use your ideas about addition and subtraction of integers to explore the relationship between these two operations.

A. Complete each number sentence.

  1. $^+5 + {}^-2 = {}^+5 - \blacksquare$

  2. $^+5 + {}^+4 = {}^+5 - \blacksquare$

  3. $^-7 + {}^-2 = {}^-7 - \blacksquare$

  4. $^-7 + {}^+2 = {}^-7 - \blacksquare$

B. What patterns do you see in the results of Question A that suggest a way to restate any addition problem as an equivalent subtraction problem?

C. Complete each number sentence.

  1. $^+8 - {}^+5 = 8 + \blacksquare$

  2. $^+8 - {}^-5 = 8 + \blacksquare$

  3. $^-4 - {}^+6 = {}^-4 + \blacksquare$

  4. $^-4 - {}^-6 = {}^-4 + \blacksquare$

D. What patterns do you see in the results of Question C that suggest a way to restate any subtraction problem as an equivalent addition problem?

E. Write an equivalent problem for each. Then find the results.

  1. $^+396 - {}^-400$

  2. $^-75.8 - {}^-35.2$

  3. $^-25.6 + {}^-4.4$

  4. $^+\frac{3}{2} - {}^+\frac{1}{4}$

  5. $^+\frac{5}{8} + {}^-\frac{3}{4}$

  6. $^-3\frac{1}{2} - {}^+5$

ACE Homework starts on page 32.

Investigation 2 Adding and Subtracting Integers   **29**

STUDENT PAGE

Notes

(29) 56

2.4 Fact Families

You can rewrite $3 + 2 = 5$ to make a fact family that shows how the addition sentence is related to two subtraction sentences.

$$3 + 2 = 5$$
$$2 + 3 = 5$$
$$5 - 3 = 2$$
$$5 - 2 = 3$$

Problem 2.4 Fact Families

A. Write a related subtraction fact for each.

1. $^-3 + {}^-2 = {}^-5$ **2.** $^+25 + {}^-32 = {}^-7$

B. Write a related addition fact for each.

1. $^+8 - {}^-2 = {}^+10$ **2.** $^-14 - {}^-20 = 6$

C. 1. Write a related sentence for each.

    a. $n - {}^+5 = {}^+35$ **b.** $n - {}^-5 = {}^+35$ **c.** $n + {}^+5 = {}^+35$

  2. Do your related sentences make it easier to find the value for n? Why or why not?

D. 1. Write a related sentence for each.

    a. $^+4 + n = {}^+43$ **b.** $^-4 + n = {}^+43$ **c.** $^-4 + n = {}^-43$

  2. Do your related sentences make it easier to find the value for n? Why or why not?

ACE Homework starts on page 32.

2.5 Coordinate Graphing

In your study of similar figures, you used positive number coordinates and arithmetic operations to locate and move points and figures around a coordinate grid. You can use negative number coordinates to produce a grid that extends in all directions.

Notes _____

Coordinate Plane

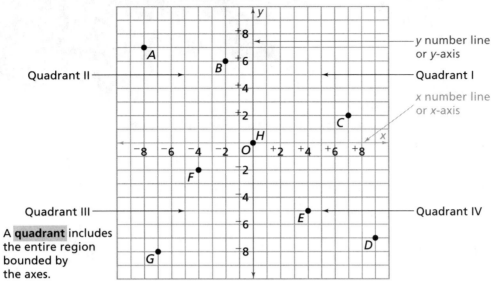

Quadrant II

y number line
or y-axis

Quadrant I

x number line
or x-axis

Quadrant III

Quadrant IV

A **quadrant** includes
the entire region
bounded by
the axes.

Problem 2.5 Coordinate Graphing

A. Write the coordinates for each point labeled with a letter.

B. What is the sign of the *x*-value and the *y*-value for any point in
Quadrant I? Quadrant II? Quadrant III? Quadrant IV?

C. The point "opposite" ($^-5$, $^+8$) has coordinates ($^+5$, $^-8$). Notice that
the sign of each coordinate in the pair changes. Write the coordinates
for the points "opposite" the labeled points. On a grid like the one
shown, graph and label each "opposite" point with a letter followed by
a tick mark. Point A′ is "opposite" point A.

D. Draw line segments connecting each pair of related points (A and A′,
B and B′, etc.). What do you notice about the line segments?

E. Plot the points in each part on a grid. Connect the points to form a
triangle. Draw each triangle in a different color, but on the same grid.

  1. ($^+1$, $^-1$)   ($^+2$, $^+3$)   ($^-4$, $^-2$)

  2. ($^-1$, $^-1$)   ($^-2$, $^+3$)   ($^+4$, $^-2$)

  3. ($^-1$, $^+1$)   ($^-2$, $^-3$)   ($^+4$, $^+2$)

  4. ($^+1$, $^+1$)   (2, $^-3$)   ($^-4$, $^+2$)

  5. How is triangle 1 related to triangle 2? How is triangle 1 related to
triangle 3? To triangle 4?

ACE Homework starts on page 32.

Investigation 2 Adding and Subtracting Integers   **31**

STUDENT PAGE

Notes _____

_____

_____

_____

Applications

1. Use your algorithms to find each sum without using a calculator.

    a. $^+12 + {}^+4$ **b.** $^+12 + {}^-4$ **c.** $^-12 + {}^+4$

    d. $^-7 + {}^-8$ **e.** $^+4.5 + {}^-3.8$ **f.** $^-4.5 + {}^+3.8$

    g. $^-250 + {}^-750$ **h.** $^-6{,}200 + {}^+1{,}200$ **i.** $^+0.75 + {}^-0.25$

    j. $^+\frac{2}{3} + {}^-\frac{1}{6}$ **k.** $^-\frac{5}{12} + {}^+\frac{2}{3}$ **l.** $^-\frac{8}{5} + {}^-\frac{3}{5}$

2. Find each sum.

    a. $^+3.8 + {}^+2.7$ **b.** $^-3.8 + {}^-2.7$

    c. $^-3.8 + {}^+2.7$ **d.** $^+3.8 + {}^-2.7$

3. Write an addition number sentence that matches each diagram.

    a.

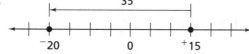

    b.

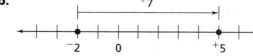

    c.

    d.

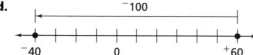

The chip board has 10 black and 13 red chips. Use the chip board for
Exercises 4 and 5.

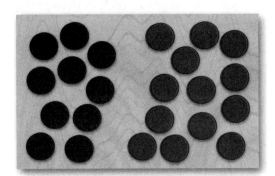

4. What is the value shown on the board?

5. Write a number sentence to represent each situation. Then find the
new value of the chip board.

   a. Remove 5 red chips from the original board.

   b. Then add 5 black chips.

   c. Then add 4 black chips and 4 red chips.

6. Use your algorithms to find each difference without using a
calculator. Show your work.

Go Online
PHSchool.com
For: Multiple-Choice Skills
   Practice
Web Code: ana-4254

   a. $^{+}12 - {}^{+}4$ b. $^{+}4 - {}^{+}12$ c. $^{-}12 - {}^{+}4$

   d. $^{-}7 - {}^{+}8$ e. $^{+}45 - {}^{-}40$ f. $^{+}45 - {}^{-}50$

   g. $^{-}25 - {}^{-}75$ h. $^{-}62 - {}^{-}12$ i. $^{+}0.8 - {}^{-}0.5$

   j. $^{+}\frac{1}{2} - {}^{+}\frac{3}{4}$ k. $^{-}\frac{2}{5} - {}^{+}\frac{1}{5}$ l. $^{-}\frac{7}{10} - {}^{+}\frac{4}{5}$

7. Find each value without using a calculator.

   a. $^{+}12 + {}^{-}12$ b. $^{+}12 - {}^{+}12$ c. $^{-}12 - {}^{+}12$

   d. $^{-}12 - {}^{-}12$ e. $^{-}12 + {}^{-}12$ f. $^{-}12 + {}^{+}12$

8. Find each value.

   a. $^{+}50 + {}^{-}35$ b. $^{+}50 - {}^{-}20$ c. $^{-}19 - {}^{+}11$

   d. $^{-}30 - {}^{+}50$ e. $^{-}35 + {}^{-}15$ f. $^{+}12 + {}^{-}18$

Investigation 2 Adding and Subtracting Integers   **33**

Notes _____

_____

_____

_____

9. Write a story about temperature, money, or game scores to represent each number sentence.

   a. $^+7 - {}^-4 = {}^+11$ b. $^-20 + {}^+n = {}^+30$ c. $^-n + {}^-150 = {}^-350$

10. Without doing any calculations, decide which will give the greater result. Explain your reasoning.

    a. $^+5,280 + {}^-768$ OR $^+5,280 - {}^-768$

    b. $^+1,760 - {}^-880$ OR $^+1,760 - {}^+880$

    c. $^+1,500 + {}^+3,141$ OR $^+1,500 - {}^-3,141$

11. Without doing any calculations, determine whether each result is positive or negative. Explain.

    a. $^-23 + {}^+19$ b. $^+3.5 - {}^-2.7$

    c. $^-3.5 - {}^-2.04$ d. $^+3.1 + {}^-6.2$

12. Find each missing part.

	Start With	Rule	End With
a.	●●	■	●●●●●●●
b.	●●●	■	●●●
c.	??	Add 5 ●	●●●
d.	?????	Subtract 5 ●	●●

13. Find each sum or difference. Show your work.

    a. $^+15 + {}^-10$ b. $^-20 - {}^+14$

    c. $^+200 - {}^-125$ d. $^-20 - {}^-14$

    e. $^-200 + {}^+125$ f. $^+7 - {}^+12$

34   Accentuate the Negative

Notes _____

_____

_____

_____

14. Below is part of a time line with three years marked.

1986   1996   2006

  a. How does 1996 relate to 1986? How does 1996 relate to 2006?

  b. Write two number sentences. One must relate 1996 to 1986. The other must relate 1996 to 2006.

  c. How are these two number sentences alike and different?

15. Compute each value.

  a. $^{+}3 + ^{-}3 + ^{-}7$

  b. $^{+}3 - ^{+}3 - ^{+}7$

  c. $^{-}10 + ^{-}7 + ^{-}28$

  d. $^{-}10 - ^{+}7 - ^{+}28$

  e. $7 - ^{+}8 + ^{-}5$

  f. $^{+}7 + ^{-}8 - ^{+}5$

  g. $^{-}97 + ^{-}35 - ^{+}10$

  h. $^{-}97 - ^{+}35 + ^{-}10$

  i. What can you conclude about the relationship between subtracting a positive number $(- \ ^{+})$ and adding a negative number $(+ \ ^{-})$ with the same absolute value?

16. Compute each value.

  a. $^{+}3 - ^{-}3 - ^{-}7$

  b. $^{+}3 + ^{+}3 + ^{+}7$

  c. $^{-}10 - ^{-}7 - ^{-}28$

  d. $^{-}10 + ^{+}7 + ^{+}28$

  e. $^{+}7 + ^{+}8 + ^{+}5$

  f. $^{+}7 - ^{-}8 - ^{-}5$

  g. $^{-}97 - ^{-}35 - ^{+}10$

  h. $^{-}97 + ^{+}35 + ^{-}10$

  i. What can you conclude about the relationship between subtracting a negative number $(- \ ^{-})$ and adding a positive number $(+ \ ^{+})$ with the same absolute value?

Multiple Choice In each set of calculations, one result is different from the others. Find the different result without doing any calculations.

17. **A.** $54 + ^{-}25$ **B.** $54 - 25$

  C. $25 - 54$ **D.** $^{-}25 + 54$

18. **F.** $^{-}6.28 - ^{-}3.14$ **G.** $^{-}6.28 + 3.14$

  H. $3.14 + ^{-}6.28$ **J.** $^{-}3.14 - ^{-}6.28$

19. **A.** $534 - 275$ **B.** $275 - 534$

  C. $^{-}534 + 275$ **D.** $275 + ^{-}534$

20. **F.** $175 + ^{-}225$ **G.** $225 - 175$

  H. $175 - 225$ **J.** $^{-}225 + 175$

Investigation 2 Adding and Subtracting Integers   **35**

Notes _____

_____

_____

_____

21. Fill in the missing information for each problem.

a. $^+5 + \frac{^-3}{4} = \blacksquare$ b. $\frac{^+4}{8} + {}^-6 = \blacksquare$ c. $^-3\frac{3}{4} - \frac{^-3}{4} = \blacksquare$

d. $^+2\frac{2}{3} - {}^+\frac{1}{3} = \blacksquare$ e. $^-2 + \blacksquare = {}^-2\frac{1}{2}$ f. $^-4.5 + \blacksquare = {}^-5$

22. **Multiple Choice** Which is the correct addition and subtraction fact family for $^-2 + {}^+3 = {}^+1$?

A. $^-2 + 3 = 1$
   $^-2 + 1 = 3$
   $3 - 1 = 2$

B. $^-2 + {}^+3 = {}^+1$
   $^-2 + 3 = 1$
   $3 - 1 = 2$

C. $^-2 + 3 = 1$
   $1 - 3 = {}^-2$
   $1 - {}^-2 = 3$

D. $1 - 3 = {}^-2$
   $1 - {}^-2 = 3$
   $3 - 1 = 2$

23. Write a related fact for each number sentence to find n. What is the value of n?

a. $n - {}^+7 = {}^+10$ b. $\frac{^-1}{2} + n = \frac{^-5}{8}$ c. $^+\frac{2}{3} - n = \frac{^-7}{9}$

24. Are $^+8 - {}^+8$ and $8 - 8$ equivalent? Explain.

25. Are $^+100 - {}^+99$ and $100 - 99$ equivalent? Explain.

26. Are the expressions in each group below equivalent? If so, which form makes the computation easiest?

a. $^+8 + {}^-10$
   $8 - {}^+10$
   $8 - 10$

b. $3 + {}^-8$
   $3 - {}^+8$
   $3 - 8$

27. Locate each pair of points on a coordinate grid. Describe the direction from the first point to the second point. Use these descriptions: to the left, to the right, downward, and upward.

a. $(^+3, {}^+2); (^-5, {}^+2)$ b. $(^-7, {}^+7); (^+3, {}^+7)$ c. $(^-8, {}^-2); (^+4, {}^-2)$

d. $(^+4, {}^+4); (^+4, {}^+20)$ e. $(^+18, {}^+8); (^+18, {}^-8)$ f. $(^-20, {}^-4); (^-20, {}^+9)$

g. Movement to the right or upward is in a positive direction. Movement to the left or downward is in a negative direction. Explain why this makes sense.

h. Now, describe the direction and the distance between the first point and the second point. For example, an answer of $^-15$ means you move in a negative direction a distance of 15. Whether the change is in the x-coordinate or the y-coordinate will tell whether $^-15$ means down 15 or to the left 15.

36   Accentuate the Negative

Notes _____

_____

_____

_____

28. a. Locate three points on a coordinate grid that could be the vertices of a right triangle.

b. Find two different points that make a right triangle with coordinates ($^-2$, $^+2$) and ($^+3$, $^+1$).

Homework Help Online
PHSchool.com
For: Help with Exercise 28
Web Code: ane-4228

Applications Connections

29. Find the opposite of each point in the graph. [Remember, the opposite of ($^+2$, $^-1$) is ($^-2$, $^+1$).]

a.

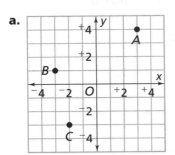

b.

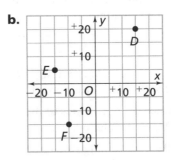

Connections

30. The Spartan Bike Shop keeps a record of their business transactions. They start their account at zero dollars. Payments represent negative transactions. Sales represent positive transactions. Write a number sentence to represent each transaction. Then find the new balance.

a. rent payment for shop: $1,800

b. payment for 20 new bicycles: $2,150

c. payment on office equipment: $675

d. business insurance for 6 months: $2,300

e. sale of 3 bicycles: $665

f. sale of two helmets and one baby seat: $95

g. Web site advertising down payment: $250

h. sale of 6 bicycles: $1,150

i. refund to an unhappy customer: $225

j. sale of 2 bicycles, two helmets, and two air pumps: $750

k. check from manufacturer for 5 bicycles returned: $530

Investigation 2 Adding and Subtracting Integers   **37**

STUDENT PAGE

STUDENT PAGE

Notes _____

_____

_____

_____

Write a number sentence for each situation in Exercises 31 and 32.

31. The air temperature drops from 94° to 72° in 15 minutes. What is the change in temperature?

32. The Teacher's Pets team has 50 points in MathMania. They miss a 200-point question. What is their new score?

33. Find four different numbers, in order from least to greatest, that lie between the two given numbers.

    a. $^-4.5$ and $^-3.5$ **b.** $^-0.5$ and $^+0.5$

34. The diagram below shows Mug Wump drawn at the center of a coordinate grid and in four other positions.

    a. Find a sequence of coordinates to draw Mug's body at the center of the grid. Make a table to keep track of the points.

    b. You can write a coordinate rule to describe the movement of points from one location to another. For example, the coordinate rule $(x, y) \rightarrow (x - {}^+2, y + {}^+3)$ moves a point (x, y) to the left 2 units and up 3 units from its original location. The coordinate rule $(x, y) \rightarrow (x + {}^+6, y - {}^+7)$ moves points of the original Mug to produce which of the other drawings?

    c. Find coordinate rules for moving the original Mug to the other positions on the grid.

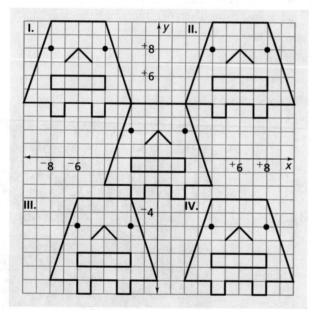

Notes _____

_____

_____

_____

Use the points in each coordinate grid to determine what scale interval was used on each axis.

35.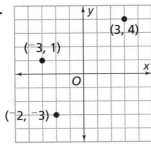

36.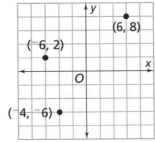

Extensions

37. Which numbers, when added to $^-15$, give a sum

    a. greater than 0   **b.** less than 0   **c.** equal to 0

38. Find the distance between each pair of numbers on a number line.

    a. $^+8, ^+4$ **b.** $^-8, ^+4$ **c.** $^+8, ^-4$

    d. $^-8, ^-4$ **e.** $^-3\frac{1}{2}, ^+\frac{3}{4}$ **f.** $^+5.4, ^-1.6$

39. Find each absolute value.

    a. $|^+8 - ^+4|$ **b.** $|^-8 - ^+4|$ **c.** $|^+8 - ^-4|$

    d. $|^-8 - ^-4|$ **e.** $|^-3\frac{1}{2} + ^+\frac{3}{4}|$ **f.** $|^+5.4 - ^-1.6|$

    g. Compare the results of parts (a)–(f) with the distances found in Exercise 38. What do you notice? Why do you think this is so?

40. Replace n with a number to make each statement true.

    a. $n + ^-18 = ^+6$ **b.** $^-24 - n = ^+12$

    c. $^+43 + n = ^-12$ **d.** $^-20 - n = ^-50$

Investigation 2 Adding and Subtracting Integers   **39**

Notes _____

_____

_____

_____

41. The table shows the profits or losses (in millions of dollars) earned by three companies from 1997 to 2006. Find the range of the annual results and the overall profit (or loss) for each company over that time period.

	Company	'97	'98	'99	'00	'01	'02	'03	'04	'05	'06
a.	Sands Motor	⁻5.3	⁻4.8	⁻7.2	⁻2.1	1.4	6.5	3.2	⁻3.5	10.2	2.4
b.	Daily Trans	6.0	3.4	⁻5.8	⁻12.3	⁻20.3	⁻1.5	2.5	9.8	19.4	32.1
c.	Sell to You	120	98	⁻20	⁻40	⁻5	85	130	76	5	⁻30

42. Julia thinks a bit more about how to use red and black chips to model operations with integers. She draws the following chip board. She decides it represents $8 \times {}^-5 = {}^-40$ and ${}^-40 \div 8 = {}^-5$.

a. Explain why Julia's reasoning makes sense.

b. Use Julia's reasoning to find each value.

   i. $10 \times {}^-5$ **ii.** $4 \times {}^-15$ **iii.** $3 \times {}^-5$

   iv. ${}^-14 \div 2$ **v.** ${}^-14 \div 7$ **vi.** ${}^-35 \div 7$

43. Starting from 0, write an addition sentence for diagram below.

a.

b.

Notes _____

_____

_____

_____

Mathematical Reflections 2

In this investigation, you applied your ideas about integers to develop algorithms for calculating any sums and differences.

Think about your answers to these questions. Discuss your ideas with other students and your teacher. Then write a summary of findings in your notebook.

1. a. How can you decide if the sum of two numbers is positive, negative, or zero without actually calculating the sum?

  b. How can you decide if the difference of two numbers is positive, negative, or zero without actually calculating the difference?

2. a. What procedure(s) will find the sum $a + b$ of two numbers where a and b represent any integer?

  b. What procedure(s) will find the difference $a - b$ of two numbers where a and b represent any integer?

3. How can any difference $a - b$ of two numbers be restated as an equivalent addition statement?

Investigation 2 Adding and Subtracting Integers **41**

Notes _____

_____

_____

_____

Answers

Investigation

ACE
Assignment Choices

Differentiated Instruction
Solutions for All Learners

Problem 2.1

Core 1, 2
Other *Applications 3, Connections 30, Extensions 37*

Problem 2.2

Core 6, 7
Other *Applications 4, 5, 8, 9; Connections 31, 32, Extensions 38, 39;* unassigned choices from previous problems

Problem 2.3

Core 10, 11
Other *Applications 12–16, Connections 33, Extensions 40;* unassigned choices from previous problems
Connecting to Prior Units 33: *Bits and Pieces I*

Problem 2.4

Core 17–22, 24–26
Other *Connections 23, Extensions 41;* unassigned choices from previous problems

Problem 2.5

Core 27, 34, 42
Other *Applications 28, 29; Connections 35, 36;* unassigned choices from previous problems

Adapted For suggestions about adapting ACE exercises, see the CMP *Special Needs Handbook.*
Connecting to Prior Units 33: *Bits and Pieces I*; 34: *Stretching and Shrinking*; 35, 36: *Variables and Patterns*

Applications

1. **a.** $^+12 + {}^+4 = {}^+16$
   b. $^+12 + {}^-4 = {}^+8$
   c. $^-12 + {}^+4 = {}^-8$
   d. $^-7 + {}^-8 = {}^-15$
   e. $^+4.5 + {}^-3.8 = {}^+0.7$
   f. $^-4.5 + {}^+3.8 = {}^-0.7$

g. $^-250 + {}^-750 = {}^-1000$
h. $^-6{,}200 + {}^+1{,}200 = {}^-5{,}000$
i. $^+0.75 + {}^-0.25 = {}^+0.5$
j. $^+\frac{2}{3} + {}^-\frac{1}{6} = {}^+\frac{3}{6} = {}^+\frac{1}{2}$
k. $^-\frac{5}{12} + {}^+\frac{2}{3} = {}^+\frac{3}{12} = {}^+\frac{1}{4}$
l. $^-\frac{8}{5} + {}^-\frac{3}{5} = {}^-\frac{11}{5}$

2. **a.** $^+3.8 + {}^+2.7 = {}^+6.5$
   b. $^-3.8 + {}^-2.7 = {}^-6.5$
   c. $^-3.8 + {}^+2.7 = {}^-1.1$
   d. $^+3.8 + {}^-2.7 = {}^+1.1$

3. **a.** $^+15 + {}^-35 = {}^-20$
   b. $^-2 + {}^+7 = {}^+5$
   c. $^-10 + {}^+14 = {}^+4$
   d. $^+60 + {}^-100 = {}^-40$

4. $^+10 + {}^-13 = {}^-3$ or $^+10 - {}^+13 = {}^-3$ or $^-13 + {}^+10 = {}^-3$

5. **a.** $^+10 + {}^-13 - {}^-5 = {}^+2$
   b. $^+10 + {}^-13 - {}^-5 + {}^+5 = {}^+7$ or $^+2 + {}^+5 = {}^+7$
   c. $^+10 + {}^-13 - {}^-5 + {}^+5 + {}^+4 + {}^-4 = {}^+7$ or $^+7 + {}^+4 + {}^-4 = {}^+7$

6. **a.** $^+12 - {}^+4 = {}^+8$
   b. $^+4 - {}^+12 = {}^-8$
   c. $-12 - {}^+4 = {}^-16$
   d. $^-7 - {}^+8 = {}^-15$
   e. $^+45 - {}^-40 = {}^+85$
   f. $^+45 - {}^-50 = {}^+95$
   g. $^-25 - {}^-75 = {}^+50$
   h. $^-62 - {}^-12 = {}^-50$
   i. $^+0.8 - {}^-0.5 = {}^+1.3$
   j. $^+\frac{1}{2} - {}^+\frac{3}{4} = {}^-\frac{1}{4}$
   k. $^-\frac{2}{5} - {}^+\frac{1}{5} = {}^-\frac{3}{5}$
   l. $^-\frac{7}{10} - {}^+\frac{4}{5} = {}^-\frac{15}{10} = {}^-\frac{3}{2}$

ACE ANSWERS 2

7. **a.** $^{+}12 + {}^{-}12 = 0$

   b. $^{+}12 - {}^{+}12 = 0$

   c. $^{-}12 - {}^{+}12 = {}^{-}24$

   d. $^{-}12 - {}^{-}12 = 0$

   e. $^{-}12 + {}^{-}12 = {}^{-}24$

   f. $^{-}12 + {}^{+}12 = 0$

8. **a.** $^{+}50 - {}^{+}35 = {}^{+}15$

   b. $^{+}50 + {}^{+}20 = {}^{+}70$

   c. $^{-}19 + {}^{-}11 = {}^{-}30$

   d. $^{-}30 + {}^{-}50 = {}^{-}80$

   e. $^{-}35 - {}^{+}15 = {}^{-}50$

   f. $^{+}12 - {}^{+}18 = {}^{-}6$

9. Answers will vary. Possible answers:

   a. The thermometer reads $^{-}4°F$ when Allison checks it in the morning and 7°F when she checks it at noon. What is the change in temperature over the course of the morning? $7° - {}^{-}4° = 11°$

   b. Stephanie spends $20 dollars to buy ingredients for her dish to sell at the bake sale. Her profit is $30. How much does her dish sell for? OR Matt writes a check for $20. He makes a deposit. He ends up with $30 more than he had before writing the check. How much does he deposit? $^{-}20 + n = 30$.

   c. In MathMania, Jacob answers his first two questions incorrectly. The second question is worth 150 points. His current score is $^{-}350$. What is the point value of his first question? $^{-}n + {}^{-}150 = {}^{-}350$.

10. **a.** $5,280 - {}^{-}768$ is greater because subtraction of a negative can be rewritten as addition $(5,280 + 768)$. This sum would be greater than the difference between 5,280 and 768 or the addition of a negative number in the case of $5,280 + {}^{-}768$.

    b. $1,760 - {}^{-}880$ is greater because it can be rewritten as addition $(1,760 + 880)$. The sum of this addition problem is then greater than the difference found in the subtraction problem of $1,760 - 880$.

    c. The two will produce the same result. $1,500 - {}^{-}3,141$ can be rewritten as $1,500 + 3,141$.

11. **a.** Negative. Use the algorithm for adding numbers with different signs: Find the difference between the two absolute values. Then take the sign of the greater absolute value. The absolute value of $^{-}23$ is greater than 19.

    b. Positive. Subtracting a negative number can be rewritten as addition. The problem becomes $3.5 + 2.7$. The sum is positive.

    c. Negative. While the subtraction of the negative can be rewritten as addition, the problem is still $^{-}3.5 + 2.04$. Thus, the algorithm for adding numbers with two different signs comes into play: Find the difference between the absolute value of the two numbers. Then take the sign of the greater absolute value. The greater absolute value in this case is 3.5, which is that of a negative number.

    d. Negative. Use the algorithm for adding numbers with different signs: Find the difference between the two absolute values. Then take the sign of the greater absolute value. The absolute value of $^{-}6.2$ is greater than the absolute value of 3.1.

12. **a.** Add 9 black chips or subtract 9 red chips

    b. Subtract 6 black chips or add 6 red chips

    c. 2 black chips

    d. 4 black chips and 1 red chip

13. **a.** $^{+}15 - {}^{+}10 = {}^{+}5$

    b. $^{-}20 + {}^{-}14 = {}^{-}34$

    c. $^{+}200 + {}^{+}125 = {}^{+}325$

    d. $^{-}20 + {}^{+}14 = {}^{-}6$

    e. $^{-}200 + {}^{+}125 = {}^{-}75$

    f. $^{+}7 + {}^{-}12 = {}^{-}5$

14. **a.** Answers may vary. Sample answer: 1996 is 10 years after 1986. 1996 is 10 years before 2006.

    b. Answers may vary. Sample answer: $1996 - 1986 = 10$; $1996 - 2006 = {}^{-}10$.

    c. Answers may vary. Possible answers: Both are 10 years apart, both involve subtraction, both have 1996 as the first number; however, they have different answers—one is $^{+}10$, and the other is $^{-}10$.

15. **a.** $^{-}7$ **b.** $^{-}7$ **c.** $^{-}45$ **d.** $^{-}45$

    e. $^{-}6$ **f.** $^{-}6$ **g.** $^{-}142$ **h.** $^{-}142$

    i. It results in the same answer. Adding a negative number is the same as subtracting a positive number when they have the same absolute value.

16. a. $^+13$ **b.** $^+13$ **c.** $^+25$ **d.** $^+25$

e. $^+20$ **f.** $^+20$ **g.** $^-72$ **h.** $^-72$

i. Subtracting a positive number or adding a negative number will result in the same answer. When you subtract a positive number, it is like adding a negative number—you can just distribute the negative sign.

17. C   **18.** J

19. A   **20.** G

21. a. $^+\frac{17}{4} = ^+4.25$ **b.** $^-\frac{44}{8} = ^-5.5$

   c. $^-3$ **d.** $^+2\frac{1}{3}$

   e. $^-\frac{1}{2}$ **f.** $^-0.5$

22. C

23. a–c. Related facts will vary. One possible answer is provided.

   a. $^+17$; $^+10 + ^+7 = n$

   b. $^-\frac{1}{8}$; $^-\frac{5}{8} - ^-\frac{1}{2} = n$

   c. $^+\frac{13}{9}$; $^-\frac{7}{9} - ^+\frac{2}{3} = ^-n$

24. Yes. Numbers without symbols are thought to be positive numbers.

25. Yes. $^+100$ and $^+99$ are just another way to write 100 and 99.

26. a. Yes. Many students will judge the addition to be the "easiest" form. Others will like the subtraction.

   b. Yes.

27. Check students' work.

   a. to the left   **b.** to the right

   c. to the right   **d.** upward

   e. downward   **f.** upward

   g. Moving to the right is moving toward positive numbers, and moving to the left is moving toward negative numbers on a number line. If we rotate the number line 90° counter-clockwise, it could be used to represent the y-axis that is perpendicular to the x-axis. Then moving upward is moving toward positive numbers, and moving downward is moving toward negative numbers on the number line.

   h. $(^+3, ^+2)$; $(^-5, ^+2)$: $^-8$; you would move in the negative direction a distance of 8 units

to get from $(^+3, ^+2)$ to $(^-5, ^+2)$.

$(^-7, ^+7)$; $(^+3, ^+7)$: $^+10$; you would move in the positive direction a distance of 10 units to get from $(^-7, ^+7)$ to $(^+3, ^+7)$.

$(^-8, ^-2)$; $(^+4, ^-2)$: $^+12$; you would move in the positive direction a distance of 12 units to get from $(^-8, ^-2)$ to $(^+4, ^-2)$.

$(^+4, ^+4)$; $(^+4, ^+20)$: $^+16$; you would move in the positive direction a distance of 16 units to get from $(^+4, ^+4)$ to $(^+4, ^+20)$.

$(^+30, ^+8)$; $(^+30, ^-8)$: $^-16$; you would move in the negative direction a distance of 16 units to get from $(^+30, ^+8)$ to $(^+30, ^-8)$.

$(^-20, ^-4)$; $(^-20, ^+9)$: $^+13$; you would move in the positive direction a distance of 13 units to move from $(^-20, ^-4)$ to $(^-20, ^+9)$.

28. a. Answers will vary. One example is $(^-2, ^+1)$, $(^+3, ^+2)$, and $(^+3, ^+1)$.

   b. Infinitely many possibilities. Points lying on the lines $y = 5x - 14$ and $y = 5x + 12$ will work. For example, $(^+2, ^-4)$, $(^-3, ^-3)$, $(^-1, ^+7)$, or $(^+4, ^+6)$.

29. a. $A'(^-3, ^-4)$, $B'(^+3, ^-1)$, $C'(^+2, ^+3)$

   b. $D'(^-15, ^-20)$, $E'(^+15, ^-5)$, $F'(^+10, ^+15)$

Connections

30. a. $0 - ^+1{,}800 = ^-\$1{,}800$

   b. $^-1{,}800 - ^+2{,}150 = ^-\$3{,}950$

   c. $^-3{,}950 - ^+675 = ^-\$4{,}625$

   d. $^-4{,}625 - ^+2{,}300 = ^-\$6{,}925$

   e. $^-6{,}925 + ^+665 = ^-\$6{,}260$

   f. $^-6{,}260 + ^+95 = ^-\$6{,}165$

   g. $^-6{,}165 - ^+250 = ^-\$6{,}415$

   h. $^-6{,}415 + ^+1{,}150 = ^-\$5{,}265$

   i. $^-5{,}265 - ^+225 = ^-\$5{,}490$

   j. $^-5{,}490 + ^+750 = ^-\$4{,}740$

   k. $^-4{,}740 + ^+530 = ^-\$4{,}210$. The balance at the end is $^-\$4{,}210$.

31. $^-22°$; $72 - 94 = ^-22$

32. $^-150$ points; $50 - 200 = 50 + ^-200 = ^-150$

33. a. Any increasing list of numbers that is greater than $^-4.5$ and less than $^-3.5$, such as $^-4.4$, $^-4.3$, $^-4.2$, $^-4.1$ or $^-3.9$, $^-3.8$, $^-3.7$, $^-3.6$.

b. Any increasing list of numbers that is greater than ⁻0.5 and less than 0.5, such as ⁻0.4, ⁻0.2, 0, 0.2 or ⁻0.45, ⁻0.15, 0.25, 0.45.

34. a.

Rule	(x, y)	(x + 6, y − 7)
Head	(⁺2, ⁺4)	(⁺8, ⁻3)
	(⁺4, ⁻2)	(⁺10, ⁻9)
	(⁺2, ⁻2)	(⁺8, ⁻9)
	(⁺2, ⁻3)	(⁺8, ⁻10)
	(⁺1, ⁻3)	(⁺7, ⁻10)
	(⁻1, ⁻2)	(⁺5, ⁻9)
	(⁻1, ⁻3)	(⁺5, ⁻10)
	(⁻2, ⁻3)	(⁺4, ⁻10)
	(⁻2, ⁻2)	(⁺4, ⁻9)
	(⁻4, ⁻2)	(⁺2, ⁻9)
	(⁻2, ⁺4)	(⁺4, ⁻3)
	(⁺2, ⁺4)	(⁺8, ⁻3)
Nose	(⁻1, ⁺1)	(⁺5, ⁻6)
	(0, ⁺2)	(⁺6, ⁻5)
	(⁺1, ⁺1)	(⁺7, ⁻6)
Mouth	(⁻2, 0)	(⁺4, ⁻7)
	(⁻2, ⁻1)	(⁺4, ⁻8)
	(⁺2, ⁻1)	(⁺8, ⁻8)
	(⁺2, 0)	(⁺8, ⁻7)
	(⁻2, 0)	(⁺4, ⁻7)
Eyes	(⁺2, ⁺2)	(⁺8, ⁻5)
	(⁻2, ⁺2)	(⁺4, ⁻5)

b. IV

c. II: $(x, y) \rightarrow (x + {}^{+}6, y + {}^{+}6)$
I: $(x, y) \rightarrow (x - {}^{+}6, y + {}^{+}6)$
III: $(x, y) \rightarrow (x - {}^{+}4, y - {}^{+}7)$

35. scale = 1

36. scale = 2

Extensions

37. a. Any numbers greater than 15, such as 15.1, 16, 200, etc.

b. Any numbers less than 15, such as 14.9, 14, ⁻2, etc.

c. 15

38. a. On a number line, ⁺8 and ⁺4 have a distance of 4 units.

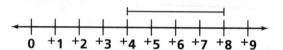

b. On a number line, ⁻8 and ⁺4 have a distance of 12 units.

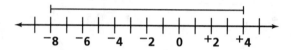

c. On a number line, ⁺8 and ⁻4 have a distance of 12 units.

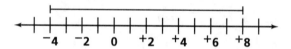

d. On a number line, ⁻8 and ⁻4 have a distance of 4 units.

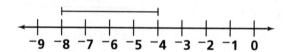

e. On a number line, $^{-}3\frac{1}{2}$ and $^{+}\frac{3}{4}$ have a distance of $\frac{17}{4}$ units. (Figure 2)

f. On a number line, ⁺5.4 and ⁻1.6 have a distance of 7 units.

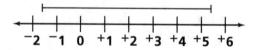

Figure 2

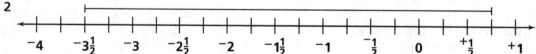

39. a. 4   **b.** 12

c. 12   **d.** 4

e. $\frac{11}{4}$ **f.** 7

g. For parts (a)–(d) and (f), the distance on the number line is the same as the absolute value computation; however, for part (e), this is not true. The absolute value computation is $2\frac{3}{4}$ or $\frac{11}{4}$. Parts (a)–(d) and (f) all deal with subtraction within the absolute value, while part (e) deals with addition. It is reasonable that the absolute value of subtraction would result in the same number as the distance on a number line because distance refers to the difference between two locations or units; thus, distance is determined by subtraction.

40. a. 24   **b.** $^-36$ **c.** $^-55$ **d.** 30

41. a. Range: 17.4; profit: 0.8

b. Range: 52.4; profit: 33.3

c. Range: 170; profit: 419

42. a. There are 8 chips, each with a value of $^-5$. Therefore, the total value is $^-5 + ^-5 + ^-5 + ^-5 + ^-5 + ^-5 + ^-5 + ^-5 = ^-40$, or $8 \times ^-5 = ^-40$. This is also true for division. If you divide $^-40$ into 8 equal parts, each part would have a value of $^-5$.

b. i. $^-50$ (Add $^-5$ ten times)

ii. $^-60$ ($^-15 + ^-15 + ^-15 + ^-15 = ^-60$)

iii. $^-15$ ($^-5 + ^-5 + ^-5 = ^-15$)

iv. $^-7$ ($^-7 + ^-7 = ^-14$, or $2 \times ^-7 = ^-14$)

v. $^-2$ ($^-2 + ^-2 + ^-2 + ^-2 + ^-2 + ^-2 + ^-2 = ^-14$, or $7 \times ^-2 = ^-14$)

vi. $^-5$ ($^-5 + ^-5 + ^-5 + ^-5 + ^-5 + ^-5 + ^-5 = ^-35$, or $7 \times ^-5 = ^-35$)

43. a. $^-7 + ^+12$

b. $^+3 + ^-13$

Possible Answers to Mathematical Reflections

1. a. If both numbers are positive, the sum will be positive. If both numbers are negative, the sum will be negative. If one number is positive and one number is negative, the sign of the sum corresponds to the number further from zero (with the greater absolute value).

b. You could rewrite the problem as an addition problem and follow the rules in part (a). Or, if the number you start with is greater than the number you subtract, the difference will be positive. If the number you start with is less than the number you subtract, the difference will be negative.

2. a. It depends on the signs of the numbers. If both numbers are positive, you just find the sum. If both numbers are negative, you just find the sum. If one number is positive and one is negative, find the difference between the absolute value of the two numbers and keep the sign of the number with the greater absolute value.

b. If both numbers are positive and the first number is greater than the second number, find the difference. The answer is positive. If both numbers are positive and the first number is less than the second number, just find the difference between the two numbers ignoring the signs, and put a negative sign on the answer. In the case of a negative minus a positive, you can rewrite the problem as an addition problem of two negatives. Then find the sum that is negative. In the case of a positive minus a negative or a negative minus a negative, it is a good idea to rewrite the subtraction problem as an addition problem and use the procedures in part (a). You will end up adding two positive numbers to get a positive.

Any subtraction problem can be rewritten as an addition problem and the procedures for addition followed.

3. For any difference of two numbers $(a - b)$, you can add the opposite $(a + ^-b)$.

Investigation 3 Multiplying and Dividing Integers

Mathematical and Problem-Solving Goals

- Use a number line/motion model to develop the relationship between repeated addition and multiplication with integers
- Develop and use algorithms for multiplying and dividing integers
- Examine number patterns to confirm the algorithm for multiplication
- Explore division of integers using the relationship between multiplication and division found in fact families
- Recognize and solve problems involving multiplication and division of integers
- Develop skill at multiplying and dividing integers

Summary of Problems

Problem 3.1 Introducing Multiplication of Integers

Problem 3.1 uses a relay race game with repeated constant running speeds, distance, and time to help students develop algorithms for multiplication. They use their intuition from the context to complete multiplication number sentences in cases involving negative numbers. They then generalize that reasoning to context-free multiplication.

Problem 3.2 Multiplication Patterns

Students look at patterns of integer multiplication as another way to confirm how the signs should behave in multiplication situations with integers.

Problem 3.3 Introducing Division of Integers

This problem builds on the algorithm for multiplication and relates multiplication and division facts to develop algorithms for division of negative numbers.

Problem 3.4 Playing the Integer Product Game

Students play and analyze a game, getting more practice with multiplying and dividing integers.

	Suggested Pacing	Materials for Students	Materials for Teachers	ACE Assignments
All	$4\frac{1}{2}$ days	Student notebooks	Blank transparencies, transparency markers	
3.1	1 day	Number Lines labsheet, Labsheets 3ACE Exercise 25 parts (a) and (b), 3ACE Exercise 25 parts (c) and (d)	Transparencies 3.1A, 3.1B, Number Lines transparency	1–3, 24, 25, 30
3.2	1 day		Transparency 3.2	4–6, 26, 31, 32
3.3	1 day	Number Lines labsheet	Transparencies 3.3A, 3.3B, Number Lines transparency	7–11, 22, 27, 28, 33
3.4	1 day	Labsheet 3.4 (1 per pair); colored pens, markers, or pencils; paper clips (2 per pair)	Transparency 3.4, 2 paper clips	12–21, 23, 29, 34, 35
MR	$\frac{1}{2}$ day			

Introducing Multiplication of Integers

Goals

- Use a number line/motion model to develop the relationship between repeated addition and multiplication with integers

- Develop and use algorithms for multiplying integers

Teacher Note: A Need for Consistency

As you and your class work through this problem, you will need to decide how you will read and write multiplication sentences. Although it does not influence the solution, 5 groups of 10 and 10 groups of 5 are two different situations. We have written 10 groups of 5 as 10 × 5 because it matches the language and notational order used in earlier sixth grade units where students explored multiplication of fractions and decimals. The Number Relay situation in Question A provides a context for labeling and making sense of what the numbers in the multiplication sentences stand for. However, as you begin to discuss the decontextualized number sentences in Question B, you will need to establish how the number sentences will be interpreted.

Launch 3.1

Look at the Did You Know? Students are given the time and distance it took two athletes (in different events) to establish a world or Olympic record.

- *How long would it take each runner to run 1,000 meters at his or her record speed?* (107.95 seconds for Michael Johnson and 106.2 seconds for Florence Griffith Joyner, if they could sustain the same pace for 1,000 meters)

As students present their strategies, note when the description indicates they were using distance, rate, and time. Be sure that they provide units for the numbers to show that they understand what is being represented.

Now move into the relay race context. Using the context of the Number Relay race, students use distance, rate, and time to determine where students participating in the Number Relay are at various times along the course. Explain how the race works. Students participate in the Number Relay race in teams of five. The race is run on a field marked from end to end with a number line from −50 to 50 with zero at the center. Three members of a team line up at the −50 yard line and two line up on the other end of the field at the 50 yard line. At the start of the relay race, the first runner at the −50 yard line runs the length of the field and hands the baton off to the second runner, who starts on the 50 yard line and runs to the other end. The relay race proceeds until the last runner gets the baton and finishes at the zero mark at the middle of the field. The team whose fifth runner gets to the zero mark at the center of the field first wins. Have students walk through a simulation if needed.

Suggested Questions Ask clarifying questions to make sure students understand the context.

- *How far does each racer run?* (Racers 1–4 run 100 m. Racer 5 runs only 50 m.)

- *Explain what the first leg of the relay would look like.* (Racer 1 takes off from the −50 point and runs as fast as possible to the 50 point and hands off the baton to Racer 2.)

- *Explain the last leg of the race.* (Racer 5 receives the baton from Racer 4 and runs from the −50 point to the 0 point.)

The goal of the problems in Question A is to have students use their knowledge of repeated addition to make sense of multiplication situations that involve both integers.

Students are asked to write number sentences for each problem in Question A. It is important that they do this in order to make sense of what happens when we multiply different combinations of integers. You might do the first problem in Question A with them to draw their attention to the relationship between repeated addition and multiplication and to make sure they are making sense of the labeling for positive and negative situations.

Ask students to look at Question A, part (1), and describe a way to figure out where Hahn will be in 10 seconds. Be sure to have students describe what each of the numbers represents in the problem.

Suggested Questions

- *What does 5 meters per second mean?* (that every 5 m takes him 1 s, or that in 1 s, he runs 5 m)

- *Which way is he running? Left or right? Positive or negative?* (right and positive)

- *What number sentence could you write to show where Hahn will be in 10 seconds if he is going to the right and passes the 0 point running 5 meters per second?* (If he runs 5 meters each second, and he runs for 10 seconds, then $5 + 5 + 5 + 5 + 5 + 5 + 5 + 5 + 5 + 5 = 50$ meter point or $10 \times 5 = 50$ meter point.)

- *What do the 5 and the 10 stand for?* (The 5 stands for the five meters that is covered each second and the 10 is for the ten seconds that Hahn is running after he passes the 0 point in the race.)

- *Suppose Hahn were running 5 meters per second to the left. How would this change the number sentence?* (The speed, or rate, would be -5 instead of 5, so you would add -5 ten times or multiply -5 times 10.)

- *What would the number sentence look like in this situation?* $[-5 + (-5) + (-5) + (-5) + (-5) + (-5) + (-5) + (-5) + (-5) + (-5) = -50$ m point or $10 \times (-5) = -50$ m point.]

- *What do the -5, the 10, and the -50 indicate in this situation?* (Hahn is running 5 m per s, but going to the left. He runs for 10 s or 10 times. At the end of the 10 s, he will be at -50 on the playing field.)

Remind students to write the mathematical sentences for Question A. This will help them see what they were thinking so they can make sense of the problems in Question B. Students have had experience finding algorithms in Investigation 2 of this unit and in previous units, so what is asked in Question B should be familiar.

Have students work in pairs and then move into groups of four to discuss their solutions.

Explore 3.1

As pairs work, make sure they are writing complete mathematical sentences reflecting totals and not just expressions. Remind them that they need to be able to explain why their solutions make sense and are reasonable.

If students are struggling to make sense of the Number Relay problems in Question A, you might want to summarize Question A before going on to Question B. If not, have students work through both Questions A and B. Remind students that when they are trying to develop algorithms in Question B, they should focus on how they solved the problems and why their solutions worked. If students are having trouble with part (5) of B, you may want to review multiplication of fractions with the class.

Summarize 3.1

Have students share their number sentences for Question A. Help them analyze how each pair of addition and multiplication sentences are related. Use the race context as a way to move toward analyzing what the numbers tell us in any multiplication sentence. A transparency of a number line will help students demonstrate what their number sentences are showing.

Suggested Questions For example, with Question A, part (2), ask:

- *What number sentences did you write for part (2)?* ($4 + 4 + 4 + 4 + 4 = 20$ or $5 \times 4 = 20$)

- *What does 5×4 mean?* (that you have 5 groups of 4)

- *What does the operation of multiplication mean?* (putting equal-sized groups together to find the total amount)

Most students think of multiplication as shorthand for writing repeated addition. If students have written repeated addition sentences instead of multiplication sentences, help them to see that their answers can also be written as multiplication sentences.

Also draw students' attention to the patterns with the combinations of positive and negative signs when you discuss problems.

Suggested Questions For example, with Question A part (3), ask:

- *What number sentences did you write for part (3)?* [$-6 + (-6) + (-6) + (-6) + (-6) + (-6) + (-6) + (-6) = -48$ or $8 \times (-6) = -48$]

- *Here you have a positive times a negative. Why is the result negative?* (Aurelia ran left or -6 m/s, and she did it for 8 s or 8 times. This means she will keep moving on the negative side of the field for 8 s.)

- *What does $8 \times (-6)$ mean?* (that you have 8 groups of -6)

For Question A part (4), students are asked to determine where Pascal was 6 seconds earlier. Students might approach this problem in many ways. They might think of it as a positive situation and then negate their answer. This makes sense since they are going backwards in time. The runner would run as fast as he would when he is going right, but you have to go in the opposite direction from 0, so the runner has to run backwards instead of forwards. Drawing attention back to the problem parameters (use negative numbers for time in the past) might help them write a number sentence with negative numbers.

Question A part (5), involves a negative integer times a negative integer because Tori is running left and the question asks about what happened 7 seconds earlier in time.

Suggested Questions As students describe their number sentences, continue to note the sign patterns as you frame your questions.

- *In Question A part (5), you have a negative direction and a negative time. Why does it make sense that this means Tori is at a positive position on the racing field?* (According to the direction, the runner should be going to the left, but since the situation asks you to go back in time, you have to move the runner to the right or into the positive end of the racing field.)

After discussing Question A, ask students:

- *How did your work in Question A help you answer the multiplication problems in Question B?* (Various answers. Students may use patterns or skip counting to think about making groups.)

Have students present their algorithms. As students talk about their algorithms, you might want to spend a few minutes using skip counting and multiples to explore sign patterns and decide if the algorithms they developed for multiplying positive and negative integers make sense. The idea here is to get students to consider what combinations of positive and negative integers give positive or negative products and why this makes sense. This is important because, when trying to write algorithms, students often become focused on the numbers and forget to consider why or if the patterns make sense.

As students present their algorithms, ask them to explain why they make sense. Refer to the context of the relay race to help students justify their algorithms.

Suggested Questions Here are some questions you might ask:

- *What is happening when you multiply a positive number by a negative number?* (The result is negative because we make groups of negative numbers.)

- *Will a negative integer times a negative integer always give a positive product?* (Yes. It is like in the Number Relay race when a runner goes to the right when going back in time. One negative would be going left, but the second negative is undoing the first one.)

For multiplication of rational numbers, use what students know about multiplication of fractions and what they have observed about signs in integer multiplication to generalize a strategy.

Going Further

- *If you had a negative times a negative times a negative, would the results be negative or positive?* (Negative because after you multiply the first two numbers, it is a positive times a negative.)

- *Is multiplication commutative for negative numbers?* [Yes. $-7 \times 5 = 5 \times (-7)$ and $-7 \times (-5) = -5 \times (-7)$. This is the same for multiplication with whole numbers. The order of the factors does not change the product.]

3.1

Introducing Multiplication of Integers

Mathematical Goals

- Use a number line/motion model to develop the relationship between repeated addition and multiplication with integers
- Develop and use algorithms for multiplying integers

Launch

Look at the Did You Know?

Explain the Number Relay race. Have students walk through a simulation. Ask clarifying questions to make sure students understand.

- *How far does each racer run?*
- *Explain the first leg of the relay.*

Do the first problem in Question A with them.

- *What does 5 meters per second mean?*
- *Which way is he running? Left or right? Positive or negative?*
- *What number sentence could you write to show where Hahn will be 10 seconds later?*
- *What do the 5 and the 10 stand for?*
- *Suppose Hahn were running 5 meters per second to the left. How would this change the number sentence?*
- *What do the −5, 10, and −50 indicate?*

Work in pairs and then move to groups of four for further discussion.

Materials
- Transparencies 3.1A, 3.1B
- Transparency markers
- Number Lines transparency

Explore

Make sure they are writing complete mathematical sentences.

If students are struggling, summarize Question A before going on to Question B.

Materials
- Number Lines labsheet

Summarize

Have students share their number sentences for Question A. Analyze how the addition and multiplication sentences are related. With part (2), ask:

- *What number sentences did you write for part (2)?*
- *What does 5 × 4 mean?*
- *What does multiplication mean?*

Draw students' attention to patterns with the combinations of positive and negative signs. For Question A part (3):

- *What number sentences did you write for part (3)?*
- *Here you have a positive times a negative. Why is the result negative?*
- *What does 8 × (−6) mean?*

Materials
- Student notebooks
- Number Lines transparency
- Labsheet 3ACE Exercise 25 parts (a) and (b)
- Labsheet 3ACE Exercise 25 parts (c) and (d)

continued on next page

continued

As students describe their number sentences, note the sign patterns.

- *In Question A part (5), you have a negative direction and a negative time. Why does it make sense that this means Tori is at a positive position on the racing field?*

Have students present their algorithms.

- *What is happening when you multiply a positive number by a negative number? A negative times a negative?*

Going Further

- *If you had a negative times a negative times a negative, would the results be negative or positive?*

- *Is multiplication commutative for negative numbers?*

ACE Assignment Guide for Problem 3.1

Core 2, 3
Other *Applications* 1; *Connections* 24, 25; *Extensions* 30

Adapted For suggestions about adapting Exercise 1 and other ACE exercises, see the CMP *Special Needs Handbook*.
Connecting to Prior Units 25: *Stretching and Shrinking*

Answers to Problem 3.1

A. These are possible answers. Students might use repeated addition sentences other than those presented, but the multiplication sentence should reflect the problem parameters.

1. $5 + 5 + 5 + 5 + 5 + 5 + 5 + 5 + 5 + 5 = 50$ m point or $10 \times 5 = 50$ m point.

2. $4 + 4 + 4 + 4 + 4 = 20$ m point or $5 \times 4 = 20$ m point.

3. $-6 + (-6) + (-6) + (-6) + (-6) + (-6) + (-6) + (-6) = -48$ m point or $8 \times (-6) = -48$ m point.

4. $-3 + (-3) + (-3) + (-3) + (-3) + (-3) = -18$ m point or $0 - 3 - 3 - 3 - 3 - 3 - 3 = -18$ m point or $6 \times (-3) = -18$ m point.

5. $5 + 5 + 5 + 5 + 5 + 5 + 5 = 35$ m point or $-7 \times (-5) = 35$ m point.

B. 1.

Group 1	Group 2	Group 3
12	-12	12
5.1	-3	28
13.5	-110	5.2

2. In Group 1, both factors are positive, and the product is positive. In Group 2, the factors have different signs, and the product is negative. In Group 3, the factors are both negative, and the product is positive.

3. Answers may vary. Possible answers:

Group 1: $5 \times 9 = 45; 7.6 \times 2 = 15.2$

Group 2: $-6 \times 3 = -18; 4 \times (-2.1) = -8.4$

Group 3: $-4 \times (-5) = 20; -3.5 \times (-6) = 21$

4. Possible algorithm: When the factors have the same sign, the product is a positive number. When the factors have opposite signs, the product is a negative number.

5. a. $\frac{-9}{8}$ or $-1\frac{1}{8}$ **b.** $\frac{3}{8}$ **c.** $\frac{-15}{8}$ or $-1\frac{7}{8}$

6. Yes, multiplication is commutative and the order of the factors does not matter. Each of the equations is correct.

Multiplication Patterns

Goal

- Examine number patterns to confirm the algorithm for multiplication

  Some students may need a second way of thinking about multiplication of integers. If your class needs more, use this problem. If they seem to understand from Problem 3.1, you can skip this problem or assign it for homework.

Launch 3.2

Display the series of equations for students to observe, including the next three in the series.

$$5 \times 5 = 25$$
$$5 \times 4 = 20$$
$$5 \times 3 = 15$$
$$5 \times 2 = 10$$
$$5 \times 1 = 5$$
$$5 \times 0 = 0$$
$$5 \times (-1) = \blacksquare$$
$$5 \times (-2) = \blacksquare$$
$$5 \times (-3) = \blacksquare$$

Suggested Questions

- *What patterns do you notice?* (Elicit a few ideas to get them started.)

- *I want you to think about how the patterns you observe help you to determine the next few equations in the series.*

  Have students work in pairs to answer the questions.

Explore 3.2

As students work on the problem, listen to the patterns they are noticing. Students may struggle with multiplying a negative by a negative in Question B. If so, suggest they think about what each sentence is saying and what seems reasonable.

Summarize 3.2

Have pairs share their observations for Question A part (1). They should notice that the first five equations are composed of two positive integers and have positive products. The last equation is the product of a positive integer and 0, which gives a product of 0. They should also see that the products become smaller as the size of the groups decreases by five at each step.

For Question A parts (2) and (3), ask students to share their solutions and explain why they are reasonable and how they fit the patterns they noticed. They should predict that the solutions to $5 \times (-1), 5 \times (-2), 5 \times (-3)$ are $-5, -10$, and -15, respectively.

In Question B part (1), students should notice that all but one equation contain a positive and a negative integer and have a negative product. The last equation is composed of a negative integer and 0 and has a product of 0. They should also see that the products are increasing as fewer groups of negatives are involved.

For Question B part (2), again have students explain why their solutions are reasonable and how they fit the patterns they noticed. They should reason that the product has to increase by 4 from the previous product and $0 + 4 = 4$. The next four equations are:

$$-1 \times (-4) = 4$$
$$-2 \times (-4) = 8$$
$$-3 \times (-4) = 12$$
$$-4 \times (-4) = 16$$

Suggested Questions Display both series of equations as you ask these questions.

- *In these two series of equations, I notice that when 0 is one of the factors in the multiplication expression, the product is 0. Is this always true? When you multiply any number by 0, will 0 always be the product?* (This is always true. 0 times any number equals 0. Thus, 0×5 means you have no groups of 5, or a product of zero.)

- *In the first series of equations, the first five equations involve multiplying two positive factors and result in a positive product. Is that always true? Does a positive factor times a positive factor always give a positive product?* (This is always true. Multiplying two positive integers can be interpreted as repeated groups of a positive amount. For example, 5×6 can be thought of as 5 groups of 6. As positive amounts are being accumulated, the answer must be positive.)

- *In the second series of equations, the first five equations involve multiplying a positive factor times a negative factor and result in a negative product. Is this always true? Does a positive factor times a negative factor always give a negative product? Explain why or why not.* (This is always true. A positive times a negative factor can be interpreted as repeated groups of negative quantities. For example, $12 \times (-2)$ can be interpreted as 12 groups of -2, which is a negative amount.)

If students offer an explanation similar to this, ask what a negative integer times a positive integer gives and why. Students often say that the product will be negative and explain this by informally using the Commutative Property $[6 \times (-3)$ is the same as $-3 \times 6]$.

- *In Question B parts (2) and (3), you multiplied two negative factors. What is the sign of the product when two negative factors are multiplied?* (The product of two negative factors is always positive.)

Thinking about multiplying a negative by a negative is abstract and quite difficult to explain for most middle school students' mathematical understanding and language. These ideas need time and reinforcement to make sense. Here are two explanations students have offered.

"To fit the pattern of the equations in Question B, the product of $-1 \times (-4)$ has to be 4."

"The problem $-1 \times (-4)$ means that you need to take the opposite of 1 group of -4."

- *When you multiply three numbers together, how do you look at the signs to predict the sign of the product?* (An even number of negative factors means the product is positive, and an odd number of negative factors means the product is negative.)

Going Further

- *Regardless of their signs, is the numerical value of the product of two numbers always the product of the two numbers? Explain.* (Students may not be able to explain clearly at this time, but help them to notice that the absolute value of the solution is always the product of the absolute values of the integers.)

- *How do you find the sign of the product?* (If the signs of the factors are alike, the product is positive. If the signs of the factors are different, the product is negative.)

Mathematical Goal

- Examine number patterns to confirm the algorithm for multiplication

Launch

Display the series of equations for students to observe, including the next three in the series.

- *What patterns do you notice?*
- *How do the patterns help you determine the next few equations in the series?*

Have students work in pairs to answer the questions.

Materials
- Transparency 3.2
- Transparency markers

Explore

As students work on the problem, listen to the patterns they are noticing.

If students struggle in Question B, suggest they think about what each sentence is saying and what seems reasonable.

Summarize

For Questions A and B, ask students to share their observations and solutions explaining why they are reasonable and how they fit the patterns they noticed.

Display both series of equations as you ask these questions.

- *If one factor is 0, what will the product be? Is this always true?*
- *The first five equations involve multiplying two positive factors and result in a positive product. Is that always true? Does a positive factor times a positive factor always give a positive product?*
- *In the second series of equations, the first five equations involve multiplying a positive factor times a negative factor and result in a negative product. Is this always true? Does a positive factor times a negative factor always give a negative product?*
- *In Question B parts (2) and (3), you multiplied two negative factors. What is the sign of the product when two negative factors are multiplied?*
- *When you multiply three numbers together, how do you look at the signs to predict the sign of the product?*

Going Further

- *Regardless of their signs, is the numerical value of the product of two numbers always the product of the two numbers? Explain.*
- *How do you find the sign of the product?*

Materials
- Student notebooks

ACE Assignment Guide for Problem 3.2

Core 4–6
Other *Connections* 26; *Extensions* 31, 32; unassigned choices from previous problems

Adapted For suggestions about adapting ACE exercises, see the CMP *Special Needs Handbook*.

Answers to Problem 3.2

A. 1. Each product decreases by 5.

  2. $5 \times (-1) = -5$
  $5 \times (-2) = -10$
  $5 \times (-3) = -15$
  Possible explanation: With each equation, there is one fewer group of 5, and 5 less than 0 is -5, 10 less than 0 is -10, and 15 less than zero is -15.

  3. $5 \times (-4) = -20$
  $5 \times (-5) = -25$
  $5 \times (-6) = -30$
  $5 \times (-7) = -35$

B. 1. $-4 \times 5 = -20$
  $-4 \times 4 = -16$
  $-4 \times 3 = -12$
  $-4 \times 2 = -8$
  $-4 \times 1 = -4$
  $-4 \times 0 = 0$

  2. The product increases each time because you are accumulating fewer negatives (one less group of -4).

  3. $-4 \times (-1) = 4$; possible explanation: With each equation, the product increases by 4, and 4 more than 0 is 4.

  4. $-4 \times (-2) = 8$
  $-4 \times (-3) = 12$
  $-4 \times (-4) = 16$
  $-4 \times (-5) = 20$

C. 1. a. 168

  b. -240

  c. -1

  2. In both settings, an even number of negative factors gives a positive product, and an odd number of negative factors gives a negative product.

3.3 Introducing Division of Integers

Goals

- Explore division of integers using the relationship between multiplication and division found in fact families

- Recognize and solve problems involving multiplication and division of integers

- Develop algorithms for dividing integers

The problem focuses on the relationship between multiplication and division. Students develop an algorithm for dividing integers based on what they know about multiplication.

Launch 3.3

Suggested Questions Write $36 \div 4 = 9$ on the board.

- *What does this sentence mean?* (This equation means that there are 36 things that are put into 4 groups of equal size and that there will be 9 things in each group—sharing reasoning. Or, it can be thought about as putting 36 things into groups of 4 and finding that there are enough to make 9 groups of 4—grouping reasoning.)

- *How are the operations of multiplication and division related?* (Multiplication and division are opposite, or inverse, operations; they undo each other. Multiplication puts equal-size groups together to find the total, and division partitions the total to find either the size of the groups or the number of groups of a given size.)

- *If multiplication and division are opposite operations that undo each other, what number sentence would undo the sentence $3 \times 12 = 36$?* (This multiplication sentence says that the total of 3 groups of 12 each is 36. If we start with the total and divide by 3, we will be partitioning the total to find the size of each equal-size group. $36 \div 3 = 12$.)

Once students are making sense of this relationship, remind students that they used fact families to write related addition and subtraction sentences in order to make sense of subtracting integers. Explain that they will use fact families and their understanding of the relationship between multiplication and division to do this problem. They will also find patterns that will help them predict the quotient of any two numbers, including integers.

The Student Edition contains examples of fact families for multiplication and division. Look for and discuss the patterns in these examples. Note what the signs are doing.

Have students work on the examples in the Getting Ready. The fact families for $-2 \times 3 = -6$ are $3 \times (-2) = -6$, $-6 \div (-2) = 3$, and $-6 \div 3 = -2$. For problem 1, draw students' attention to the notion that we know that $48 \div 8 = 6$, so the missing factor should be a 6. Students can then use their multiplication algorithm to decide whether the 6 should be positive or negative. Since two factors with opposite signs give a negative product, the 6 should be negative.

Answers to the Getting Ready

1. $8 \times (-6) = -48$
2. $-12 \times (-9) = 108$
3. $6 \times (-13) = -78$

Have them work in pairs and then in groups to answer the questions.

Explore 3.3

As students work on the problem, listen to the patterns they are noticing. If they are struggling, you might stop them after Question B part (1), summarize what they have done so far, and then have them complete the problem.

Summarize 3.3

Have students display their solutions to Question A. If there are disagreements about any of the solutions, have students discuss their solutions and explain why they make sense.

Facilitate a conversation to help students generalize some rules for dividing positive and negative integers. Look for opportunities to talk about fact families and the relationship between multiplication and division.

Suggested Questions Use questions like these as students discuss their solutions.

- *How did you decide if the quotient is positive or negative?*

- *What multiplication problems are related to this division problem?*

- *How can you use your algorithm for multiplication to decide whether the quotient is positive or negative?*

For Question B, ask students to share their answers and their algorithms for the problems in each of the three groups. Look for opportunities to highlight how multiplication and division are related. Also try to bring out the nature of division problems as sharing or grouping problems when working with integers.

- *Why is the rule "a negative divided by a negative is positive" reasonable?* (For example, with $-96 \div (-4) = 24$, you can interpret the problem as having a total of -96 and wanting to find out how many groups of -4 you can make by partitioning the total into equal groups. You can make 24 groups of -4 from -96. Also, the quotient must be positive because -4 must be multiplied by a positive 24 to have a product of -96.)

- *How can you find the quotient when you divide a negative integer by a positive integer? For example, why does it make sense that $-99 \div 11 = -9$?* (You can think of $-99 \div 11 = -9$ as sharing a total of -99 into 11 groups of equal size. The groups must be negative amounts, since you are sharing a negative amount, so the quotient must be negative.)

- *How can you find the quotient when you divide a positive number by a negative number?* (This is difficult to think about. It helps to use fact families and division as the inverse of multiplication. For example, if you want to show $99 \div (-11) = -9$, you know that $-11 \times (-9) = 99$. Then you know that $99 \div (-11)$ must be -9 and $-99 \div 11$ must equal -9.)

- *We have found that addition and multiplication are commutative. Is division commutative?* (No. $-2 \div 3 \neq 3 \div (-2)$.
  $-2 \div 3 = \frac{-2}{3}$, which is greater than -1, while
  $3 \div -2 = \frac{3}{-2}$ or $-1\frac{1}{2}$, which is less than -1.
  You can place the numbers on the number line to see for sure. So the order in which you divide does matter.)

3.3 Introducing Division of Integers

Mathematical Goals

- Explore division of integers using the relationship between multiplication and division found in fact families
- Recognize and solve problems involving multiplication and division of integers
- Develop algorithms for dividing integers

Launch

Write 36 ÷ 4 = 9 on the board.

- *What does this sentence mean?*
- *How are the operations of multiplication and division related?*
- *If multiplication and division are opposite operations that undo each other, what number sentence would undo 3 × 12 = 36?*

Discuss the patterns in the examples in the Student Edition. Note what the signs are doing.

Have students work on the examples in the Getting Ready.

For problem 1, draw students' attention to the notion of using 48 ÷ 8. Students can then use their multiplication algorithm to decide whether the 6 should be positive or negative.

Have them work in pairs and then in groups to answer the questions.

Materials
- Transparencies 3.3A, 3.3B
- Transparency markers

Explore

As students work on the problem, listen to the patterns they are noticing. If they are struggling, you might stop them after Question B part (1), summarize what they have done so far, and then have them complete the problem.

Materials
- Number Lines labsheet

Summarize

Have students display the solutions to Question A. If there are disagreements, have students discuss their solutions and explain why they make sense.

Help students generalize some rules for dividing positive and negative integers. Use questions like these as students discuss their solutions.

- *How did you decide if the quotient is positive or negative?*
- *What multiplication problems are related to this division problem?*
- *How can you use your algorithm for multiplication to decide whether the quotient is positive or negative?*

For Question B, ask students to share their answers and their algorithms for the problems in each of the three groups.

Materials
- Student notebooks
- Number Lines transparency

continued on next page

- *Why is the rule "a negative divided by a negative is positive" reasonable?*

- *How can you find the quotient when you divide a negative integer by a positive integer? For example, why does it make sense that $-99 \div 11 = -9$?*

- *How can you find the quotient when you divide a positive number by a negative number?*

- *We have found that addition and multiplication are commutative. Is division commutative?*

ACE Assignment Guide for Problem 3.3

Core 7, 8, 33
Other *Applications* 9–11; *Connections* 22, 27, 28; unassigned choices from previous problems

Adapted For suggestions about adapting ACE exercises, see the CMP *Special Needs Handbook*.
Connecting to Prior Units 27: *Data About Us,* 28: *Bits and Pieces II* and *Bits and Pieces III*

Answers to Problem 3.3

A. 1. $15 \div 5 = 3$ (15 m ÷ 5 s = 3 m/s)

   2. $-12 \div 3 = -4$ (-12 m ÷ 3 s = -4 m/s)

   3. $-50 \div 5 = -10$ (Pascal left the point -50 ten seconds before she passed 0.)
   $-24 \div 5 = \frac{-24}{5}$ or $-4\frac{4}{5}$ or -4.8
   (Pascal left the point -24, 4.8 s before he passed 0.)

   4. $-40 \div (-8) = 5$ (It will take Tori 5 s.)

B. 1.

Group 1	Group 2	Group 3
4	-13	15
10.2	-3.75	1.2
0.5	-2	6

2. In Group 1, the dividend and divisor are both positive, and the quotient is positive. In Group 2, the dividend and divisor have different signs, and the quotient is negative. In Group 3, the dividend and divisor are both negative, and the quotient is positive.

3. Answers may vary. Possible answers:

   Group 1: $24 \div 6 = 4$; $3.2 \div 8 = 0.4$

   Group 2: $36 \div (-9) = -4$; $6 \div (-2) = -3$

   Group 3: $-60 \div (-12) = 5$; $-21 \div (-3) = 7$

4. Possible answer: Divide the numbers as if they are unsigned and then decide which sign to use. If the signs are the same, the quotient will be positive. If the signs are different, the quotient will be negative.

5. a. -2

   b. $\frac{2}{3}$

   c. $-3\frac{1}{3}$

6. No, division is not commutative. For example, $-2 \div 3$ is $\frac{-2}{3}$, or about -0.66, while $3 \div (-2)$ is -1.5, or $-1\frac{1}{2}$. When you change the order of the numbers, you get different quotients. Students should provide two examples like this one. You might suggest to them that they use negative as well as positive numbers in their examples.

Goal

- Develop skill at multiplying and dividing integers

This problem helps students practice their multiplication and division of integers with a version of the Product Game from the sixth grade *Prime Time* unit. You may want to remind students by showing the game that appears in the *Prime Time* Student Edition.

Launch 3.4

Display the Integer Product Game Board and ask members of the class to explain the rules for the factor game. If students do not remember the rules from *Prime Time*, they can read them in the Student Edition. The rules for both games are the same.

Play one game with the class to be sure everyone understands how to play the game.

Suggested Questions

- *What factors can I put paper clips on to get a product of −12?* (2 × (−6); −2 × 6; 3 × (−4); −3 × 4; or the reverse of each.)

- *What numbers divide −12 equally?* (1, −1, 2, −2, 3, −3, 4, −4, 6, −6, 12, −12)

- *How are these two lists related?* (The list of factors for the Integer Product game is contained in the longer list.)

This is a two-person game. Have students pair up and play the game a few times.

Explore 3.4

Some teachers find it productive to let teams of two play against each other. This allows the teammates to share and discuss strategies. Remind students to write down any patterns or winning strategies that they discover.

- *As you play the game, think about these questions.*

Write the following questions on the board:

- *Is it better to go first or second? Why?* (Second, because you do not get a square if you play first.)

- *What is the best move if you are second?* (Go for a square toward the middle because you can complete a string with that number in more directions.)

As students are playing and analyzing the game, look for students who are using various strategies. It may be helpful to have students record mathematical sentences to show their thinking. In some cases, students might be using multiplication to guide their moves, and at other times division. Look for examples of both to bring out during the summary.

Summarize 3.4

Begin by discussing any strategies for playing and winning the game that students discovered. Here are some strategies students have found.

> "It is better to go second, because if you go first, you really don't get to make a move on the board."

> "There are more ways to get certain numbers than there were in the old games. For example, 6 can be made by 1 × 6 and 2 × 3, but it can also be made by −1 × (−6) and −2 × (−3). This version of the game makes you more aware of where the markers are on the board. I needed to carefully check all the possibilities before making my move so that I would have more choices on my next turn or not set up my opponent for a good move."

> "I tried to get products that would block my opponent."

Guide the discussion of strategies to bring out the notion that when using positive and negative products, you have many more combinations to consider than you do when the Product Game is played with non-negative numbers. Question B can help get at this idea.

Suggested Questions Some questions you might ask regarding the questions in Question B are:

- *How would the pairs of factors in Question B compare to the list of factor pairs you could make if the game only used positive numbers?* (There are twice as many factor pairs for every positive product.)

In Questions C and D, help students connect their approaches back to their algorithms. Writing number sentences for their verbal descriptions might be helpful. Here is part of a conversation that a class had about Question C:

Classroom Dialogue Model

Mbato *If −4 is the starting number, I can make the product −16.*

Teacher *How do you know that −16 will work? What would you put your other paper clip on?*

Mbato *Since I have a negative number and I am trying to get a negative number, I have to multiply a negative number by a positive number to get a negative number. −4 × 4 = −16.*

Teacher *So you decided that since a negative times a positive is a negative that you should choose a factor that is positive. So, Mbato used this part of your algorithm for multiplying. [Teacher points to the algorithms that are on a poster displayed in the room.]*

Check for Understanding
Write on the overhead or board: $5 \times (-6) = -30$.

- *Use the words* factor, divisor, multiple, product, *and* divisible by, *to write four statements about the sentence* $5 \times (-6) = -30$. (Some possible sentences are:
−30 is a multiple of 5 and of −6.
5 is a factor of −30.
−6 is a divisor of −30.
−30 is divisible by 5.
−30 is divisible by −6.
The product of 5 and −6 is −30.)

3.4 Playing the Integer Product Game

Mathematical Goal

- Develop skill at multiplying and dividing integers

Launch

Display the Integer Product Game Board and ask members of the class to explain the rules of the game. If students do not remember the rules from *Prime Time*, they can read them in the Student Edition.

Play one game with the class to be sure everyone understands how to play.

- *What factors can I put paper clips on to get a product of −12?*
- *What numbers divide −12 equally?*
- *How are these two lists related?*

Have students pair up and play the game a few times.

Materials
- Transparency 3.4
- Transparency markers
- 2 paper clips

Explore

Remind students to write down any patterns or winning strategies that they discover.

- *As you play the game, think about these questions.*

Display the following questions:

- *Is it better to go first or second? Why?*
- *What is the best move if you are second?*

As students are playing and analyzing the game, look for those who are using various strategies. Have students record mathematical sentences to show their thinking. Look for examples of students using both multiplication and division to bring out during the summary.

Materials
- Labsheet 3.4
- Paper clips (2 per pair)
- Colored pens, markers, or pencils

Summarize

Begin by discussing any strategies for playing and winning the game that students discovered.

Guide the discussion to bring out that when using positive and negative products, you have many more combinations to consider than you do when the Product Game is played with non-negative numbers. Question B can help get at this idea.

- *How would the pairs of factors in Question B compare to the list of factor pairs you could make if the game only used positive numbers?*

In Questions C and D, help students connect back to their algorithms. Writing number sentences for their verbal descriptions might be helpful.

Materials
- Student notebooks

continued on next page

continued

Check for Understanding

Write on the overhead or board: $5 \times (-6) = -30$.

- *Use the words* factor, divisor, multiple, product, *and* divisible by, *to write four statements about the sentence* $5 \times (-6) = -30$.

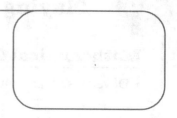

ACE Assignment Guide
for Problem 3.4

Core 12–20, 29
Other *Applications* 21; *Connections* 23; *Extensions* 34, 35; unassigned choices from previous problems

Adapted For suggestions about adapting ACE exercises, see the CMP *Special Needs Handbook*.
Connecting to Prior Units 29: *Bits and Pieces II* and *Bits and Pieces III*

Answers to Problem 3.4

A. Variable answers. See Summary for some possibilities.

B. 1. 1 and 5, −1 and −5

　　2. 2 and −6, −2 and 6, 3 and −4, −3 and 4

　　3. 2 and 6, −2 and −6, 3 and 4, −3 and −4

　　4. 5 and −5

C. 4 by putting clip on −1, −4 by putting clip on 1, 8 by putting clip on −2, −8 by putting clip on 2, 12 by putting clip on −3, −12 by putting clip on 3, 16 by putting on −4, −16 by putting clip on 4, 20 by putting clip on −5, −20 by putting clip on 5, 24 by putting clip on −6, −24 by putting clip on 6.

D. 1. Move the marker from −2 to 3 ($-5 \times 3 = -15$).

　　2. Move the marker from −3 to 3 or move the marker from −2 to 2 ($3 \times (-2) = -6$ or $-3 \times 2 = -6$).

　　3. You should avoid factors of 24 that are positive or negative. For this game board, you want to avoid 6, −6, 4, and −4.

The student edition pages for this investigation begin on the next page.

Notes _____
_____
_____
_____

Multiplying and Dividing Integers

Some Notes on Notation

You have been writing integers with raised signs to avoid confusion with the symbols for addition and subtraction. However, most computer software and most writing in mathematics do not use raised signs.

Positive numbers are usually written without a sign.

$$^+3 = 3 \text{ and } ^+7.5 = 7.5$$

Negative numbers are usually written with a dash like a subtraction sign.

$$^-3 = -3 \text{ and } ^-7.5 = -7.5$$

From now on, we will use this notation to indicate a negative number.

This can be confusing if you don't read carefully. Parentheses can help.

$$^-5 - {}^-8 = -5 - -8 = -5 - (-8)$$

The subtraction symbol also indicates the opposite of a number. For example, -8 represents the opposite of 8. The expression $-(-8)$ represents the opposite of -8.

$$-(-8) = 8$$

For multiplication, you can use a raised dot symbol.

$$3 \times 5 = 3 \cdot 5$$

Notes _____

_____

_____

_____

In this investigation, you will use time, distance, speed, and direction to think about multiplication and division of integers. You will also look at number patterns and develop algorithms for multiplying and dividing these numbers.

Did You Know?

Michael Johnson set a world record by running 400 meters in 43.18 seconds at the world track championships in 1999. Florence Griffith Joyner set an Olympic record when she ran 100 meters in 10.62 seconds in 1988.

How long would it take each runner to run 1,000 meters at his or her record speed?

 **For:** Information about track
Web Code: ane-9031

Investigation 3 Multiplying and Dividing Integers   **43**

Notes _____

_____

_____

_____

3.1 Introducing Multiplication of Integers

The math department at Everett Middle School sponsors a contest called the Number Relay. A number line measured in meters is drawn on the school field. Each team has five runners. Runners 1, 3, and 5 stand at the −50 meter line. Runners 2 and 4 stand at the 50 meter line.

Team 1

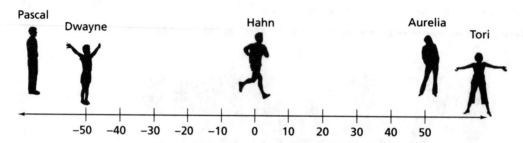

For Team 1:

- Hahn starts and runs from −50 to 50. He tags Aurelia.
- Aurelia runs back from 50 to −50. She tags Dwayne.
- Dwayne runs from −50 to 50. He tags Tori.
- Tori runs from 50 to −50. She tags Pascal.
- Pascal runs from −50 to the finish line at position 0.

The team whose final runner reaches the 0 point first wins.

Notes _____

_____

_____

_____

A. Write number sentences that express your answers to these questions. Use positive numbers for running speeds to the right and negative numbers for running speeds to the left. Use positive numbers for time in the future and negative numbers for time in the past. Each runner runs at a constant speed.

1. Hahn passes the 0 point running 5 meters per second to the right. Where is he 10 seconds later?

2. Dwayne passes the 0 point running 4 meters per second to the right. Where is he 5 seconds later?

3. Aurelia passes the 0 point running to the left at 6 meters per second. Where is she 8 seconds later?

4. Pascal passes the 0 point running to the right at 3 meters per second. Where was he 6 seconds earlier?

5. Tori passes the 0 point running to the left at 5 meters per second. Where was she 7 seconds earlier?

B. 1. Find the products in each group below.

Group 1	Group 2	Group 3
4×3	$4 \times (-3)$	$-4 \times (-3)$
5.1×1	-1.5×2	$-7 \times (-4)$
3×4.5	$10 \times (-11)$	$-5.2 \times (-1)$

2. Describe what the examples in each group have in common.

3. Use your answer to part (2) to write two problems for each group.

4. Describe an algorithm for multiplying rational numbers.

5. Use your strategy to multiply these rational numbers.

  a. $-1\frac{1}{2} \times \frac{3}{4}$ **b.** $-\frac{1}{2} \times \left(-\frac{3}{4}\right)$ **c.** $2\frac{1}{2} \times \left(-\frac{3}{4}\right)$

6. Is multiplication commutative? Does the order of factors matter? For example, are these multiplication sentences correct?

$$2 \cdot 3 \stackrel{?}{=} 3 \cdot 2$$
$$-2 \times (-3) \stackrel{?}{=} -3 \times (-2)$$
$$-2 \times 3 \stackrel{?}{=} 3 \times (-2)$$

ACE Homework starts on page 50.

Notes _____

_____

_____

_____

After studying the relay race problem, some students started playing with number patterns to see whether what they found in the relay race made sense. Study the equations below. Look for patterns.

$$5 \times 5 = 25$$
$$5 \times 4 = 20$$
$$5 \times 3 = 15$$
$$5 \times 2 = 10$$
$$5 \times 1 = 5$$
$$5 \times 0 = 0$$

Problem 3.2 Multiplication Patterns

A. 1. How do the products change as the numbers multiplied by 5 get smaller?

2. Predict $5 \times (-1), 5 \times (-2)$, and $5 \times (-3)$. Explain your reasoning.

3. Write the next four equations in the pattern.

B. 1. Complete the equations below.

$$(-4) \times 5 = \blacksquare$$
$$(-4) \times 4 = \blacksquare$$
$$(-4) \times 3 = \blacksquare$$
$$(-4) \times 2 = \blacksquare$$
$$(-4) \times 1 = \blacksquare$$
$$(-4) \times 0 = \blacksquare$$

2. How do the products change as the numbers multiplied by -4 get smaller?

3. Predict $-4 \times (-1)$. Explain.

4. Write the next four equations in the pattern.

C. 1. Find each value.

a. $7 \times (-8) \times (-3)$

b. $-12 \times (-5) \times (-4)$

c. $\frac{1}{2} \times \left(-\frac{2}{3}\right) \times 3$

2. How do the patterns you found in this problem compare to the algorithm from Problem 3.1?

ACE **Homework starts on page 50.**

Notes

3.3 Introducing Division of Integers

You know there is a relationship between addition and subtraction facts. A similar relationship exists between multiplication and division. For any multiplication fact, we can write another multiplication fact and two different related division facts. Here are three examples.

$\left(\text{Remember that you can write } 15 \div 3 \text{ as a fraction, } \frac{15}{3}.\right)$

Example 1	Example 2	Example 3
$5 \times 3 = 15$	$6 \times (-3) = -18$	$4.5 \times (-2) = -9$
$3 \times 5 = 15$	$-3 \times 6 = -18$	$-2 \times 4.5 = -9$
$15 \div 3 = 5 \text{ or } \frac{15}{3} = 5$	$-18 \div (-3) = 6 \text{ or } \frac{-18}{-3} = 6$	$-9 \div (-2) = 4.5 \text{ or } \frac{-9}{-2} = 4.5$
$15 \div 5 = 3 \text{ or } \frac{15}{5} = 3$	$-18 \div 6 = -3 \text{ or } \frac{-18}{6} = -3$	$-9 \div 4.5 = -2 \text{ or } \frac{-9}{-4.5} = -2$

Getting Ready for Problem 3.3

- What patterns do you see in Examples 1–3?
- Write a fact family for $-2 \times 3 = -6$.
- How can you use what you know about the relationship between multiplication and division facts to help you solve these problems?

    1. $8 \times \blacksquare = -48$

    2. $\blacksquare \times (-9) = 108$

    3. $6 \times (-13) = \blacksquare$

You can use this relationship and your ideas from the Number Relay questions to develop algorithms for dividing integers.

Investigation 3 Multiplying and Dividing Integers   **47**

Notes

A. Recall the Number Relay from Problem 3.1. Write division sentences that express your answers to the questions below.

1. Dwayne goes from 0 to 15 in 5 seconds. At what rate (distance per second) does he run?

2. Aurelia reaches −12 only 3 seconds after passing 0. At what rate does she run to the left?

3. Pascal passes 0 running to the right at a rate of 5 meters per second. When did he leave the point −50? When did he leave the point −24?

4. Tori wants to reach the point −40 running to the left at 8 meters per second. How long will it take her from the time she passes 0?

B. 1. Find the quotients in each group below.

Group 1	Group 2	Group 3
12 ÷ 3	39 ÷ (−3)	−45 ÷ (−3)
51 ÷ 5	−15 ÷ 4	−4.8 ÷ (−4)
4.5 ÷ 9	10 ÷ (−5)	−72 ÷ (−12)

2. Describe what the examples in each group have in common.

3. Use your answer to part (2) to write two problems for each group.

4. Describe an algorithm for dividing rational numbers.

5. Use your strategy to divide these rational numbers.

a. $-1\frac{1}{2} \div \frac{3}{4}$ **b.** $-\frac{1}{2} \div \left(-\frac{3}{4}\right)$ **c.** $2\frac{1}{2} \div \left(-\frac{3}{4}\right)$

6. Is division commutative? Does $-2 \div 3 = 3 \div (-2)$? Give two other examples to support your answer.

ACE Homework starts on page 50.

3.4 Playing the Integer Product Game

You have developed algorithms for multiplying and dividing integers. You will need them to play the Integer Product Game.

The game board consists of a list of factors and a grid of products. To play, you need a game board, two paper clips, and colored markers or chips.

Notes

Integer Product Game Rules

1. Player A puts a paper clip on a number in the factor list.
2. Player B puts the other paper clip on any number in the factor list, including the number chosen by Player A. Player B then marks the product of the two factors on the product grid.
3. Player A moves *either one* of the paper clips to another number. He or she then marks the new product with a different color than Player B.
4. Each player takes turns moving a paper clip and marking a product. A product can only be marked by one player.
5. The winner is the first player to mark four squares in a row (up and down, across, or diagonally).

Integer Product Game Board

–36	–30	–25	–24	–20	–18
–16	–15	–12	–10	–9	–8
–6	–5	–4	–3	–2	–1
1	2	3	4	5	6
8	9	10	12	15	16
18	20	24	25	30	36

Factors:

–6 –5 –4 –3 –2 –1 1 2 3 4 5 6

Problem 3.4 Multiplying Integers

Play the Integer Product Game with positive and negative factors. Look for strategies for picking the factors and products.

A. What strategies did you find useful in playing the game? Explain.

B. What pair(s) of numbers from the factor list will give each product?

1. 5   **2.** −12   **3.** 12   **4.** −25

C. Your opponent puts a paper clip on −4. List five products that you can form. Tell where you need to put your paper clip in each case.

D. Describe the moves to make in each case.

1. The paper clips are on −5 and −2. You want a product of −15.

2. The paper clips are on −3 and −2. You want a product of −6.

3. Your opponent will win with 24. What numbers should you avoid with your paper clip moves?

active math online

For: Integer Product Game Activity
Visit: PHSchool.com
Web Code: and-4304

ACE Homework starts on page 50.

Notes _____

_____

_____

_____

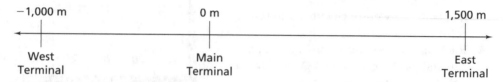

Applications

1. At some international airports, trains carry passengers between the separate terminal buildings. Suppose that one such train system moves along a track like the one below.

```
   -1,000 m              0 m                        1,500 m
      |                   |                            |
   West                 Main                         East
   Terminal             Terminal                     Terminal
```

a. A train leaves the main terminal going east at 10 meters per second. Where will it be in 10 seconds? When will it reach the east terminal?

b. A train passes the main terminal going east at 10 meters per second. Where was that train 15 seconds ago? When was it at the west terminal?

c. A train leaves the main terminal going west at 10 meters per second. Where will it be in 20 seconds? When will it reach the west terminal?

d. A train passes the main terminal going west at 10 meters per second. When was it at the east terminal? Where was it 20 seconds ago?

Notes _____

_____

_____

_____

The dot patterns illustrate commutative properties for operations on whole numbers. Write a number sentence for each case.

2.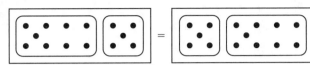

3.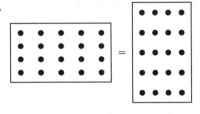

4. Find each value.

  a. $7 \cdot 2$ **b.** $-7 \times (-2)$ **c.** $7 \times (-2)$

  d. -7×2 **e.** $8 \cdot 2.5$ **f.** $-9 \times (-4)$

  g. $12 \times (-3)$ **h.** -1.5×4 **i.** 3.5×7

  j. $-8.1 \cdot (-1)$ **k.** $1 \times (-6)$ **l.** $-2\frac{1}{2} \times 1$

5. Find the values for each pair.

  a. $4 \times (-3)$ and -3×4 **b.** $2 \cdot (-4)$ and $-4 \cdot 2$

  c. $-2 \times (-3)$ and $-3 \times (-2)$ **d.** $\frac{1}{5} \times \left(-\frac{4}{9}\right)$ and $-\frac{4}{9} \times \frac{1}{5}$

  e. What can you conclude about multiplication with negative numbers?

6. Tell whether each product is greater than or less than zero.

  a. $5 \times (-7)$ **b.** $-3.2 \cdot 1.5$

  c. $10.5 \times (-4)$ **d.** $-2 \times (-3) \times (-1)$

  e. $-\frac{2}{3} \cdot 2\frac{3}{4}$ **f.** $-\frac{3}{4} \times \left(-1\frac{5}{6}\right) \times \left(-\frac{7}{4}\right)$

  g. $-\frac{3}{4} \times \left(-1\frac{5}{6}\right) \times \frac{7}{4}$ **h.** $-\frac{3}{4} \times \left(-1\frac{5}{6}\right) \times \left(-\frac{7}{4}\right) \times \left(-2\frac{3}{8}\right)$

  i. $\frac{3}{4} \cdot \left(-1\frac{5}{6}\right) \cdot \frac{7}{4} \cdot \left(-2\frac{3}{8}\right)$ **j.** $\frac{3}{4} \times 1\frac{5}{6} \times \frac{7}{4} \times \left(-2\frac{3}{8}\right)$

7. You have located fractions such as $-\frac{5}{7}$ on a number line. You have also used fractions to show division: $\frac{-5}{7} = -5 \div 7$ and $\frac{5}{-7} = 5 \div (-7)$. Tell whether each statement is *true* or *false*. Explain.

  a. $\frac{-1}{2} = \frac{1}{-2}$ **b.** $-\frac{1}{2} = \frac{-1}{-2}$

Investigation 3 Multiplying and Dividing Integers   **51**

Notes _____

_____

_____

_____

8. Find a value for *n* to make each sentence true.

    a. $24 \div 2 = n$ **b.** $-24 \div (-2) = n$

    c. $24 \div n = -12$ **d.** $n \div 2 = -12$

    e. $5 \div 2.5 = n$ **f.** $-12 \div n = 3$

    g. $n \div (-3) = -4$ **h.** $-16 \div \frac{1}{4} = n$

Write four related multiplication and division facts for each set of integers.

Sample $27, 9, 3$

$$9 \times 3 = 27$$
$$3 \times 9 = 27$$
$$27 \div 9 = 3$$
$$27 \div 3 = 9$$

9. $7, -3, -21$ **10.** $-4, -5, 20$ **11.** $1.5, -3, -4.5$

Without doing any calculations, determine whether each expression is greater than, less than, or equal to 0.

12. $-1,105.62 \div 24.3$ **13.** $0 \times (-67)$

14. $-27.5 \times (-63)$ **15.** $0 \div 89$

16. $-54.9 \div (-3)$ **17.** $-2,943 \times 1.06$

18. Use the algorithms you developed to find each value. Show your work.

    a. $12 \cdot 9$ **b.** $5 \times (-25)$ **c.** $-220 \div (-50)$

    d. $48 \div (-6)$ **e.** $-63 \div 9$ **f.** $\frac{2}{-3} \times \left(-\frac{4}{5}\right)$

    g. $\frac{-99}{33}$ **h.** $-2.7 \div (-0.3)$ **i.** -36×5

    j. $52.5 \div (-7)$ **k.** $-2\frac{1}{2} \times \left(-\frac{2}{3}\right)$ **l.** $9 \div 5$

    m. $-9 \times (-50)$ **n.** $-\frac{96}{24}$ **o.** $6 \times 1\frac{1}{2}$

    p. $-\frac{5}{8} \times \frac{8}{5}$ **q.** $4 \times \left(-1\frac{1}{4}\right)$ **r.** $-2.5 \times 2\frac{1}{5}$

Go Online
PHSchool.com
For: Multiple-Choice Skills Practice
Web Code: ana-4354

Multiple Choice Find each value.

19. $-24 \div 4$

    A. -96 **B.** -6 **C.** 6 **D.** 96

20. $-10 \times (-5)$

    F. -50 **G.** -2 **H.** 2 **J.** 50

Notes _____

_____

_____

_____

21. Chris and Elizabeth are making a version of the Integer Product Game in which players need three products in a row to win. What six factors do they need for their game?

Homework Help Online
PHSchool.com
For: Help with Exercise 21
Web Code: ane-4321

Chris and Elizabeth's Product Game

4	−4	6	−6
9	−9	10	−10
15	−15	25	−25

Factors:

Connections

22. Multiply or divide. Show your work.

a. 52×75 **b.** $52 \times (-75)$ **c.** $-2{,}262 \div (-58)$

d. $\frac{2}{3} \times \frac{4}{5}$ **e.** $-9{,}908 \div 89$ **f.** $-7.77 \div (-0.37)$

g. -34×15 **h.** $53.2 \div (-7)$ **i.** $-\frac{2}{3} \times \frac{6}{8}$

j. $90 \div 50$ **k.** $-90 \times (-50)$ **l.** $-108 \div 24$

m. $19.5 \div (-3)$ **n.** -8.4×6 **o.** $6 \times 2\frac{1}{2}$

p. $-3\frac{2}{3} \times (-9)$ **q.** $-4 \times \left(1\frac{1}{4}\right)$ **r.** $-2.5 \times -2\frac{1}{5}$

23. Find integers to make each sentence true.

a. ■ × ■ = 30   **b.** ■ × ■ = −30   **c.** −24 ÷ ■ = ■

24. On Tuesday, the temperature changes −2°F per hour from noon until 10:00 a.m. the next morning. The temperature at noon on Tuesday is 75°F.

a. What is the temperature at 4:00 p.m. on Tuesday?

b. What is the temperature at 9:00 a.m. on Wednesday?

c. Plot the (time, temperature) data on a coordinate graph using noon Tuesday as time 0.

d. Describe the pattern of points. How does the pattern relate to the rate of change in temperature?

Investigation 3 Multiplying and Dividing Integers   **53**

Notes _____

_____

_____

_____

25. The diagram below shows Mug Wump drawn on a coordinate grid.

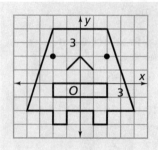

a. Complete the (x, y) column of a table like the one shown to record coordinates of key points needed to draw Mug, or copy your table from Exercise 34 of Investigation 2.

Coordinates for Mug and Variations

Rule	(x, y)	(2x, 2y)	(−2x, −2y)
Head Outline	(−4, −2)		
	(−2, −2)		
	(−2, −3)		
Nose	(−1, 1)		
Mouth	(−2, −1)		
Eyes	(−2, 2)		

b. Suppose you make scale drawings with rules $(x, y) \rightarrow (2x, 2y)$ and $(x, y) \rightarrow (-2x, -2y)$. Give coordinates for the images of Mug.

c. On graph paper, plot the images of Mug Wump produced by the new sets of coordinates in part (b).

d. Compare the length, width, and area of Mug's mouth to those of the figures drawn in part (c). Explain how you could have predicted those results by studying the coordinate rules for the drawings.

26. Write a number sentence to represent each situation.

    a. The Extraterrestrials have a score of −300. They answer four 50-point questions incorrectly. What is their new score?

    b. The Super Computers answer three 100-point questions incorrectly. They now have 200 points. What was their score before answering the three questions?

    c. The Bigtown Bears football team are at the 25-yard line. In the next three plays, they lose an average of 4 yards per play. Where are the Bears after the three plays?

    d. A new convenience store wants to attract customers. For a one-day special, they sell gasoline for $0.25 below their cost. They sell 5,750 gallons that day. How much money do they lose?

27. The list below gives average temperatures (in °C) for Fairbanks, Alaska, for each month of the year, from January through December.

    −25, −20, −13, −2, 9, 15, 17, 14, 7, −4, −16, −23

    a. What is the median?

    b. What is the range?

    c. What is the mean?

    d. Number the months from 1 (for January) through 12 (for December). Plot a graph of the (month, temperature) data.

28. Find the sum, difference, product, or quotient without using a calculator.

    a. $-5 - 18$ **b.** $-23 + 48$ **c.** $\frac{3}{4} \times \left(\frac{-5}{9}\right)$

    d. $119 + (-19.3)$ **e.** $-1.5 - (-32.8)$ **f.** $12 \div 15$

    g. $-169 \div (-1.3)$ **h.** $0.47 - 1.56$ **i.** $6 \times (-3.5)$

    j. $\frac{2}{-3} \div \frac{5}{6}$ **k.** $\frac{7}{12} - \left(-\frac{2}{3}\right)$ **l.** $-\frac{4}{5} + \left(-\frac{1}{4}\right)$

Notes _____

_____

_____

_____

29. Estimate the sum, difference, product, or quotient.

 a. $-52 - 5$ **b.** $-43 + (-108)$ **c.** $2\frac{3}{4} \times \left(-\frac{5}{9}\right)$

 d. $79 + (-25.3)$ **e.** $-12.5 - (-37.3)$ **f.** $89 \div 15$

 g. $-169 \div (-13)$ **h.** $6.3 - 1.86$ **i.** $61 \times (-3.9)$

 j. $-\frac{2}{3} \div 1\frac{5}{6}$ **k.** $5\frac{7}{12} - \left(-\frac{2}{3}\right)$ **l.** $-\frac{4}{5} \div \left(-\frac{1}{4}\right)$

Extensions

30. Many towns and small cities have water towers to store water. Water flows into and out of the towers all day long. Generally, flow out of the tower is greatest during the hours when most people are awake and active. The flow into the tower is greatest at night when most people are asleep.

The table below shows the water flow into and out of a water tower for a given time period. For each part, write a number sentence to find the change in water supply over the given time.

Water Tower Water Flow

	Water Flow In (gallons per hour)	Water Flow Out (gallons per hour)	Time (hours)
a.	5,000	0	4
b.	4,000	0	7
c.	0	7,500	3
d.	5,000	3,000	6.5

Notes
_____
_____
_____
_____

31. To add 5 + 3 + 2, you might think that it is easier to add the 3 + 2 and then add the answer to the 5. The mathematical property that allows you to change the grouping of addends (or factors) is called the *Associative Property*.

Test the Associative Property for addition and multiplication of integers by simplifying below. Find the values within the parentheses first. When you need a grouping symbol like parentheses inside another parentheses, you can use brackets to make it easier to read. For example, $(4 - (-6))$ can be written as $[4 - (-6)]$.

a. $[3 \times (-3)] \times 4$ and $3 \times (-3 \times 4)$

b. $(-5 \times 4) \times (-3)$ and $-5 \times [4 \times (-3)]$

c. $[-2 \times (-3)] \times (-5)$ and $-2 \times [-3 \times (-5)]$

d. $(3 \times 4) \times (-5)$ and $3 \times [4 \times (-5)]$

e. $[3 + (-3)] + 4$ and $3 + (-3 + 4)$

f. $(-5 + 4) + (-3)$ and $-5 + [4 + (-3)]$

g. $[-2 + (-3)] + (-5)$ and $-2 + [-3 + (-5)]$

h. $(3 + 4) + (-5)$ and $3 + [4 + (-5)]$

i. Does the Associative Property work for addition and multiplication of integers?

32. Explain how each rule changes the original shape, size, and location of Mug Wump.

a. $(x, y) \rightarrow (-x, y)$ **b.** $(x, y) \rightarrow (x, -y)$

c. $(x, y) \rightarrow (-0.5x, -0.5y)$ **d.** $(x, y) \rightarrow (-0.5x, y)$

e. $(x, y) \rightarrow (-3x, -3y)$ **f.** $(x, y) \rightarrow (-3x + 5, -3y - 4)$

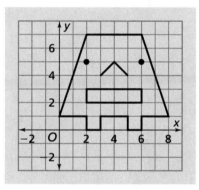

Investigation 3 Multiplying and Dividing Integers   **57**

Notes _____

_____

_____

_____

33. Tell whether each statement is *true* or *false*. Explain.

　　a. $-1 = -1 + 0$　　**b.** $-3\frac{3}{8} = -\frac{21}{8}$　　**c.** $-6.75 = -6 + \left(-\frac{3}{4}\right)$

34. Find a set of numbers to make a Sum Game. Each sum on the board should be the sum of two numbers (possibly a single number added to itself). Each pair of numbers should add to a sum on the board.

　　Hint: You need 11 numbers, all with different absolute values.

Sum Game Board

-24	-22	-20	-18	-16	-14
-12	-11	-10	-9	-8	-7
-6	-5	-4	-3	-2	-1
0	1	2	3	4	5
6	7	8	9	10	11
12	14	16	18	20	22

Numbers:

35. Write a story for a problem that is answered by finding the value of *n*.

　　a. $-4n = -24$　　　　　　　**b.** $\frac{n}{2} = 16$

Notes _____

_____

_____

_____

Mathematical Reflections 3

In the problems of this investigation you studied ways to use multiplication and division of integers to answer questions about speed, time, distance, and direction of motion. You used the results of those calculations to develop algorithms for multiplying and dividing any two integers. The questions that follow should help you to summarize your findings.

Think about your answers to these questions. Discuss your ideas with other students and your teacher. Then write a summary of your findings in your notebook.

1. How do you find the product of two numbers when
   a. both are positive?
   b. one is positive and one is negative?
   c. both are negative?
   d. one is 0?

2. How do you find the quotient of two numbers when
   a. both are positive?
   b. one is positive and the other is negative?
   c. both are negative?
   d. the numerator is 0?

3. Suppose three numbers are related by an equation in the form $a \times b = c$ where a, b, and c are not equal to 0. Write two equivalent number sentences using division.

Notes _____

_____

_____

_____

Investigation 3

ACE Assignment Choices

Differentiated Instruction
Solutions for All Learners

Problem 3.1

Core 2, 3
Other *Applications* 1; *Connections* 24, 25; *Extensions* 30

Problem 3.2

Core 4–6
Other *Connections* 26; *Extensions* 31, 32; unassigned choices from previous problems

Problem 3.3

Core 7, 8, 33
Other *Applications* 9–11; *Connections* 22, 27, 28; unassigned choices from previous problems

Problem 3.4

Core 12–20, 29
Other *Applications* 21; *Connections* 23; *Extensions* 34, 35; unassigned choices from previous problems

Adapted For suggestions about adapting Exercise 1 and other ACE exercises, see the CMP *Special Needs Handbook*.
Connecting to Prior Units 25: *Stretching and Shrinking;* 27: *Data About Us;* 28, 29: *Bits and Pieces II* and *Bits and Pieces III*

Applications

1. **a.** In 10 seconds, it will be at 100 meters (10 m/s × 10 s = 100 m). It will reach the east terminal in 150 seconds (1,500 m ÷ 10 m/s = 150 s).

   b. 15 seconds ago, it was at −150 meters or 150 meters to the west of the main terminal [10 m/s × (−15 s) = −150 m]. It was at the west terminal about 100 seconds ago (−1,000 m ÷ 10 m/s = −100 s).

   c. In 20 seconds, it will be at −200 meters or 200 meters to the west (−10 m/s × 20 s = −200 m). It will reach

the west terminal in 100 seconds [−1,000 m ÷ (−10 m/s) = 100 s].

   d. It was at the east terminal 150 seconds ago or −150 seconds [1,500 m ÷ (−10 m/s) = −150 s]. 20 seconds ago, it was at 200 meters or 200 meters to the east of the main terminal [−10 m/s × (−20 s) = 200 m].

2. $9 + 5 = 5 + 9$

3. $4 \times 5 = 5 \times 4$

4. **a.** $7 \cdot 2 = 14$ **b.** $-7 \times (-2) = 14$
   c. $7 \times (-2) = -14$ **d.** $-7 \times 2 = -14$
   e. $8 \times 2.5 = 20$ **f.** $-9 \times (-4) = 36$
   g. $12 \times (-3) = -36$ **h.** $-1.5 \times 4 = -6$
   i. $3.5 \times 7 = 24.5$ **j.** $-8.1 \times (-1) = 8.1$
   k. $1 \times (-6) = -6$ **l.** $-2\frac{1}{2} \times 1 = -2\frac{1}{2}$

5. **a.** −12 and −12 **b.** −8 and −8
   c. 6 and 6 **d.** $\frac{-4}{45}$ and $\frac{-4}{45}$
   e. All the answers are equal, so multiplication with negative numbers is commutative.

6. **a.** < **b.** < **c.** < **d.** <
   e. < **f.** < **g.** > **h.** >
   i. > **j.** <

7. **a.** True. You can either distribute the negative sign (that is out front) to the numerator or the denominator. In either of the forms, it will still be a negative answer.
   $-1 \div 2 = 1 \div (-2)$

   b. False. $-(\frac{1}{2}) = -0.5$, but $\frac{-1}{-2} = 0.5$. In $\frac{-1}{-2}$, both numbers are negative, and a negative divided by a negative equals a positive.
   $-1 \div (-2) = 0.5$

8. **a.** 12 **b.** 12 **c.** −2 **d.** −24
   e. 2 **f.** −4 **g.** 12 **h.** −64

9. $7 \times (-3) = -21; -3 \times 7 = -21;$
   $-21 \div 7 = -3; -21 \div (-3) = 7$

10. $-4 \times (-5) = 20; -5 \times (-4) = 20;$
    $20 \div (-4) = -5; 20 \div (-5) = -4$

ACE ANSWERS 3

11. $1.5 \times (-3) = -4.5$; $-3 \times 1.5 = -4.5$; $-4.5 \div 1.5 = -3$; $-4.5 \div (-3) = 1.5$.

12. Less than 0 (A negative number divided by a positive number will result in a negative product.)

13. 0 (anything multiplied by 0 is 0)

14. Greater than 0 (a negative multiplied by a negative results in a positive number.)

15. 0 (0 divided by any non-zero number, regardless of sign, is 0)

16. Greater than 0 (A negative number divided by a negative number results in a positive)

17. Less than 0 (a negative and a positive multiplied together results in a negative number)

18. a. 108   **b.** -125 **c.** 4.4

    d. -8 **e.** -7 **f.** $\frac{8}{15}$

    g. -3 **h.** 9   **i.** -180

    j. -7.5 **k.** $\frac{5}{3}$ **l.** 1.8

    m. 450   **n.** -4 **o.** 9

    p. -1 **q.** -5 **r.** -5.5

19. B   **20.** J

21. $\pm 2, \pm 3, \pm 5$

Connections

22. a. $52 \times 75 = 3{,}900$

    b. $52 \times (-75) = -3{,}900$

    c. $-2{,}262 \div (-58) = 39$

    d. $\frac{2}{3} \times \frac{4}{5} = \frac{8}{15}$

    e. $-9{,}908 \div 89 \approx -111.326$

    f. $-7.77 \div (-0.37) = 21$

    g. $-34 \times 15 = -510$

    h. $53.2 \div (-7) = -7.6$

    i. $\frac{-2}{3} \times \frac{6}{8} = \frac{-12}{24} = \frac{-1}{2}$

    j. $90 \div 50 = 1.8$

    k. $-90 \times (-50) = 4{,}500$

    l. $-108 \div 24 = -4.5$

    m. $19.5 \div (-3) = -6.5$

    n. $-8.4 \times 6 = -50.4$

o. $6 \times 2\frac{1}{2} = 15$

p. $-3\frac{2}{3} \times (-9) = 33$

q. $-4 \times (1\frac{1}{4}) = -5$

r. $-2.5 \times -2\frac{1}{5} = +5.5$

23. Answers may vary. Possible answers:

    a. $-6, -5$ or $-10, -3$

    b. $6, -5$ or $-10, 3$

    c. $8, -3$ or $-6, 4$

24. a. There are 4 h between noon and 4:00 P.M. In 4 h, the temperature changes $4 \times (-2) = -8°F$, so the temperature at 4:00 P.M. was $75 + (-8) = 67°F$.

    b. There are 21 h between noon and 9:00 A.M. In 21 h, the temperature changes $21 \times (-2) = -42°F$, so the temperature at 9:00 A.M. was $75 + (-42) = 33°F$.

    c.

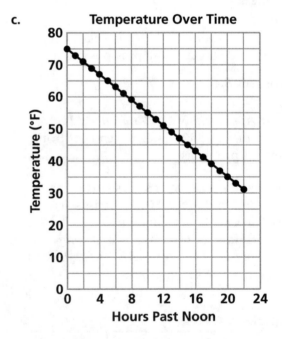

    d. The graph (above) decreases over time (if the points were connected). The points decrease at a rate of 2°F per hour.

25. a–b.

Coordinates for Mug and Variations

Rule	(x, y)	(2x, 2y)	(−2x, −2y)
Head Outline	(−4, −2)	(−8, −4)	(8, 4)
	(−2, −2)	(−4, −4)	(4, 4)
	(−2, −3)	(−4, −6)	(4, 6)
	(−1, −3)	(−2, −6)	(2, 6)
	(−1, −2)	(−2, −4)	(2, 4)
	(1, −2)	(2, −4)	(−2, 4)
	(1, −3)	(2, −6)	(−2, 6)
	(2, −3)	(4, −6)	(−4, 6)
	(2, −2)	(4, −4)	(−4, 4)
	(4, −2)	(8, −4)	(−8, 4)
	(2, 4)	(4, 8)	(−4, −8)
	(−2, 4)	(−4, 8)	(4, −8)
	(−4, −2)	(−8, −4)	(8, 4)
Nose	(−1, 1)	(−2, 2)	(2, −2)
	(0, 2)	(0, 4)	(0, −4)
	(1, 1)	(2, 2)	(−2, −2)
Mouth	(−2, −1)	(−4, −2)	(4, 2)
	(2, −1)	(4, −2)	(−4, 2)
	(2, 0)	(4, 0)	(−4, 0)
	(−2, 0)	(−4, 0)	(4, 0)
	(−2, −1)	(−4, −2)	(4, 2)
Eyes	(−2, 2)	(−4, 4)	(4, −4)
	(2, 2)	(4, 4)	(−4, −4)

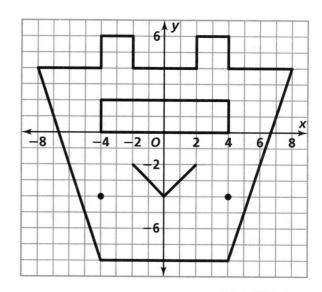

c.

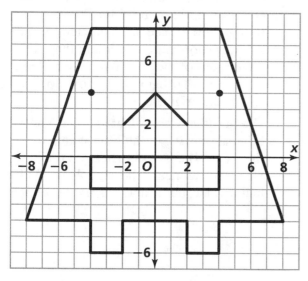

d. The coefficient of 2 makes the original Mug Wump twice as long and twice as wide. The coefficient of −2 makes the original Mug Wump twice as long and twice as wide, but the negative coefficient makes the new Mug Wump upside down. The area is 4 times as large as the original. This could have been predicted from studying the coordinate rules by using scale factors. The scale factor was 2 for length and width and, therefore, $2 \times 2 = 4$ for area.

26. a. −500 points; $-300 + [4 \times (-50)] = -500$ or $-300 - (4 \times 50) = -500$

b. 500 points; $X + (3 \times -100) = 200$; $X = 200 + 300$; $X = 500$

c. 13-yd line; $25 - (3 \times 4) = 13$ or $25 + [3 \times (-4)] = 13$

d. lost $1,437.50; $5,750 \times (-0.25) = -1,437.50$

27. a. The temperatures measured in °C from the lowest to highest are: −25, −23, −20, −16, −13, −4, −2, 7, 9, 14, 15, 17. The median falls between the sixth and seventh temperatures, or between −2 and −4, which is a median of −3°C.

b. The temperature goes from −25°C to 17°C, giving a range of 42°C.

c. The sum of all the temperatures is −41°C, giving a mean temperature of $-41°C \div 12 \approx -3.4°C$.

d.

Average Temperature in Alaska

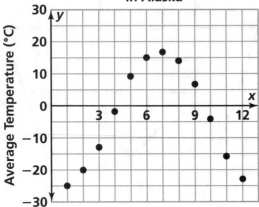

28. a. $-5 - 18 = -23$

b. $-23 + 48 = 25$

c. $\frac{3}{4} \times \left(-\frac{5}{9}\right) = -\frac{5}{12}$

d. $119 + (-19.3) = 99.7$

e. $-1.5 - (-32.8) = 31.3$

f. $12 \div 15 = 0.8$ or $\frac{4}{5}$

g. $-169 \div (-1.3) = 130$

h. $0.47 - 1.56 = -1.09$

i. $6 \times (-3.5) = -21$

j. $\frac{2}{-3} \div \frac{5}{6} = -\frac{4}{5}$

k. $\frac{7}{12} - \left(-\frac{2}{3}\right) = \frac{15}{12}$

l. $-\frac{4}{5} + \left(-\frac{1}{4}\right) = -\frac{21}{20}$

29. a. -57

b. about -150

c. about -1.5; $[3 \times (-\frac{1}{2})]$

d. about 55; $[80 + (-25)]$

e. about 25; $(-12.5 + 37.5)$

f. about 6; $(90 \div 15)$

g. about 13

h. about 4.1; $(6 - 1.9)$

i. about -244; $[61 \times (-4)]$

j. about $-\frac{1}{3}$; $(-\frac{2}{3} \div 2)$

k. about $6\frac{1}{2}$; $(5\frac{1}{2} + 1)$

l. about 4; $[-1 \div (-\frac{1}{4})]$

Extensions

30. a. $5{,}000 \times 4 = 20{,}000$ gal of water will be added.

b. The supply will be $4{,}000 \times 7 = 28{,}000$ gal greater.

c. The change is $-7{,}500 \times 3 = -22{,}500$ gal. So, the supply will decrease by 22,500 gal.

d. The change is $[5{,}000 + (-3{,}000)] \times 6.5 = 13{,}000$. So, the supply will be 13,000 gal more at the end of the 6.5-hour period.

31. a. $-9 \times 4 = -36$ and $3 \times (-12) = -36$

b. $-20 \times (-3) = 60$ and $-5 \times (-12) = 60$

c. $6 \times (-5) = -30$ and $-2 \times 15 = -30$

d. $12 \times (-5) = -60$ and $3 \times (-20) = -60$

e. $0 + 4 = 4$ and $3 + 1 = 4$

f. $-1 + (-3) = -4$ and $-5 + 1 = -4$

g. $-5 + (-5) = -10$ and $-2 + (-8) = -10$

h. $7 + (-5) = 2$ and $3 + (-1) = 2$

i. The Associative Property does work for addition and multiplication of integers.

32. a. The negative x-coordinate reflects the original drawing of the Mug Wump over the y-axis, creating a mirror image of the same size and shape in the second quadrant.

b. The negative y-coordinate reflects the original drawing of the Mug Wump over the x-axis, creating an upside-down mirror image of the same size and shape in the fourth quadrant.

c. The negative x- and y-coordinates reflect the original drawing of the Mug Wump over the x-axis and across the y-axis to create an upside-down Mug Wump in the third quadrant. The 0.5 coefficient on each x- and y-coordinate will shrink the original dimensions of the Mug Wump in half and create a similar figure that is one-fourth the size of the original.

d. The negative x-coordinate reflects the original drawing of the Mug Wump over the y-axis. The 0.5 coefficient on the x-coordinate means the Mug Wump will be half as wide, but just as tall, as the original.

e. The negative *x*- and *y*-coordinates reflect the original drawing of the Mug Wump over the *x*-axis and across the *y*-axis to create an upside-down Mug Wump in the third quadrant. The coefficient of 3 on each *x*- and *y*-coordinate will increase the original Mug Wump dimensions to create a similar figure three times as tall and three times as wide as the original.

f. The negative *x*- and *y*-coordinates reflect the original drawing of Mug Wump over the *x*-axis and across the *y*-axis to create an upside-down Mug Wump in the third quadrant. The coefficient of 3 on each *x*- and *y*-coordinate will increase the original Mug Wump dimensions to create a similar figure three times as tall and three times as wide as the original. Once the image of an upside-down Mug Wump that is three times as wide and three times as tall is created, the 5 added to the *x*-coordinate will slide the Mug Wump over five units to the right. The 4 subtracted from the *y*-coordinate will slide the Mug Wump down 4 units.

33. a. True. Zero added to any number, positive or negative, will not change the value of the number.

b. False. $-3\frac{3}{8} = -\frac{27}{8}$

c. True.

34. $-12, -10, -8, -4, -2, 0, 1, 3, 7, 9, 11$

35. a. The temperature dropped 4°F every hour, until it had dropped 24°F. For how many hours did the temperature drop 4°F? $-4n = -24, n = 6$ hours

b. When Jayne and Stewart split their earnings from yard work on Saturday, they each received $16. How much did they earn together from the yard work? $\frac{n}{2} = 16$, $n = \$32$

Possible Answers to Mathematical Reflections

1. a. The product will be positive if the two numbers have the same sign, so a positive number multiplied by a positive number will give a positive product. Simply multiply the two factors while disregarding the sign and then make the product positive.

b. The product will be negative if the two numbers have opposite signs. Simply multiply the two factors while disregarding the signs and then make the product negative.

c. The product will be positive if the two numbers have the same sign, so a negative number multiplied by a negative number will give a positive product. Simply multiply the two factors while disregarding the sign and then make the product positive.

d. When any number, positive or negative, is multiplied by zero, the product will be zero.

2. a. The quotient will be positive if the two numbers have the same sign, so a positive number divided by a positive number will give a positive quotient. Simply divide the two numbers while disregarding the sign and then make the quotient positive.

b. The quotient will be negative if the two numbers have opposite signs. Simply divide the two numbers while disregarding the sign and then make the quotient negative.

c. The quotient will be positive if the two numbers have the same sign, so a negative number divided by a negative number will give a positive quotient. Simply divide the two numbers while disregarding the sign and then make the quotient positive.

d. The quotient will be zero if the numerator is zero. If you divide zero by a non-zero number, such as $0 \div 6$, you get zero. If you divide a non-zero number by zero, such as $3 \div 0$, no answer makes sense. Division by zero is impossible. If we consider $3 \div 0 = p$ and use what we know about fact families, we can write two related multiplication problems: $0 \times p = 3$ and $p \times 0 = 3$. It is not possible to multiply a number by zero and get a non-zero number.

3. $c \div b = a$ and $c \div a = b$ OR $12 \div 3 = 4$ and $12 \div 4 = 3$ can be written for $3 \times 4 = 12$.

Note: This only works for non-zero numbers.

Mathematical and Problem-Solving Goals

- Explore the use of the order of operations to order computation in problems
- Model the Distributive Property with areas of rectangles that have edges subdivided
- Develop and use the Distributive Property of multiplication over addition
- Develop and use the Distributive Property of multiplication over subtraction
- Use the Distributive Property to solve problems

This investigation asks students to compare some algebraic properties of the operations on integers to those of the system of only positive numbers. It also summarizes notation used, the convention of order of operations, and provides further practice with all four operations. The properties and conventions are examined in three problems that compare whole numbers, positive rational numbers, and positive and negative rational numbers with respect to the Distributive Property. The Commutative Property was introduced earlier, and the Associative Property was explored in an ACE exercise. However, major work on it is delayed until further units. This is not intended to be a full-scale treatment of field properties.

Summary of Problems

Problem 4.1 Order of Operations

Students discover a need for an agreed-upon order of operations to establish uniqueness of solution for computations.

Problem 4.2 Distributing Operations

This problem introduces students to the Distributive Property with addition through finding expressions for areas of rectangles with subdivided edges.

Problem 4.3 The Distributive Property and Subtraction

This problem defines the Distributive Property for multiplication over addition and subtraction and examines how it can be used to simplify calculations. Students both expand and factor expressions and solve contextualized problems.

Unit Project

You may want to launch the unit project around this time. See page 12 of this Teacher's Guide for an overview.

	Suggested Pacing	Materials for Students	Materials for Teachers	ACE Assignments
All	$4\frac{1}{2}$ days	Calculators	Blank transparencies and transparency markers	
4.1	1 day		Transparencies 4.1A , 4.1B	1, 2, 8–29, 36–43
4.2	2 days		Transparencies 4.2A, 4.2B	3, 4, 30–32, 44
4.3	1 day		Transparency 4.3	5–7, 33–35, 45, 46
MR	$\frac{1}{2}$ day			

Order of Operations

Goal

- Explore the use of the order of operations to order computation in problems

Launch 4.1

Use the Getting Ready to engage the class in what the challenge of the problem will be. In the Getting Ready, two students do a computation and get different answers because they did the computations in a different order. Have the students look at the problem and make their own predictions about which should be correct. They can use the context to guide the appropriate order of operations. Then turn to a discussion of the rules for the order of operations and the examples given. Return to the Getting Ready as an example and decide with the class what the answer is according to the agreed-upon rules of order. Pedro did the multiplication and then the addition, so he did the correct order of operations.

Remind students to go back to these rules as needed throughout the problem.

Talk a bit about the use of parentheses with your students. Make sure that they understand parentheses as a grouping symbol that indicates that what is in the parentheses is to be treated as a single entity. This means that you need to compute what is in the parentheses first. It also means that you can insert parentheses to make sure the expressions you write reflect the order of operations you intend. For example, for the expression $5 + (-2) \times (-3)$, you get 11 if you follow the order of operations. But suppose you want the expression to mean adding first and then multiplying. You can insert parentheses to override the order of operations. Then $(5 + (-2)) \times (-3) = -9$ because parentheses are computed first. This will be useful in Question C of Problem 4.1. Also remind students that when you need a grouping symbol like parentheses inside another parentheses, you can use brackets to make it easier to read. So, $(5 + (-2))$ becomes $[5 + (-2)]$. Since students will be working with exponents, review this notation with a few simple examples

like: $3^2 = 3 \times 3, 2^3 = 2 \times 2 \times 2$ and $2^4 = 2 \times 2 \times 2 \times 2$.

Working in pairs is a good classroom arrangement for this problem.

Explore 4.1

Ask students to say in words how the mathematical sentences they write or have to interpret should be computed. For example, Question A part (1) might be read, "Find the product of -6 and 4. Subtract this product from 5. Then add -3 to the difference."

For Question C, suggest they use the order of operations rules to find an answer. Then, think about which operation can make an answer greater. Multiplication can, so you need to make the factors you multiply as great as possible. For part (2), this would suggest adding the 46 and 2.8 before you multiply. And it also suggests that you do not want to subtract the 2 from the 7 before you multiply because this decreases a factor. So $(46 + 2.8) \times 7 - 2$ should be greater. It gives a product of 339.6, whereas, without the parentheses, you get 63.6. To make it even less, you make the factors as small as possible. This suggests putting parentheses around the $7 - 2$ so that you multiply by a smaller number. With parentheses, $46 + 2.8 \times (7 - 2)$ gives 60 as the answer.

When most students have completed at least one problem in Question C, begin the whole class summary.

Summarize 4.1

Go over Question A and use the discussion to summarize the strategies students have used so far to help them both write and interpret mathematical sentences. Throughout the summary, have students say in words how the expressions they have written or been given should be computed.

Question B provides practice in using the rules for the order of operations. It also makes the point that these rules are for any numbers, including fractions.

Each of the problems in Question C asks students to find the greatest and least values. Ask students to share strategies that helped them use parentheses to make answers less and strategies that helped make answers greater.

Question D is a challenge for the students because of its length and complexity. If all students have not started this problem, give them a few minutes now to work on it before discussing it. Be sure to discuss this problem in steps so that students can reason through it and apply the order of operations when the string of symbols is long.

Have students display their thinking.

There are no parentheses, so you start with the exponent of 2 on the 7.

$$3 + 4 \times 5 \div 2 \times 3 - 7^2 + 6 \div 3$$
$$3 + 4 \times 5 \div 2 \times 3 - 49 + 6 \div 3$$

Then you continue with multiplication and division.

$$3 + 4 \times 5 \div 2 \times 3 - 49 + 6 \div 3$$

$$3 + 20 \div 2 \times 3 - 49 + 2$$

$3 + 10 \times 3 - 49 + 2$	Multiplication and division
$3 + 30 - 49 + 2$	Addition and subtraction
-14	

So: $3 + 4 \times 5 \div 2 \times 3 - 7^2 + 6 \div 3 = -14$

Check for Understanding

For each example, tell the sequence of computations needed to get the correct answer and give the answer.

1. $2^2 + 7 \times (-3) - 5$

2. $(2^2 + 7) \times (-3) - 5$

3. $(2^2 + 7) \times (-3 - 5)$

Note: $(-1)^2 = 1$ but $-1^2 = -1$.
The first, $(-1)^2$, means $(-1)(-1) = 1$.
The second means $-(1)(1) = -1$.

4.1 Order of Operations

Mathematical Goal

- Explore the use of the order of operations to order computation in problems

Launch

Use the Getting Ready to engage the class in what the challenge of the problem will be. Have the students look at the problem and make their own predictions about which should be correct. Then turn to a discussion of the rules for the order of operations and the examples given. Return to the Getting Ready as an example and decide with the class what the answer is according to the agreed-upon rules of order.

Remind students to go back to these rules as needed throughout the problem.

Talk about the use of parentheses. Make sure that they understand parentheses as a grouping symbol that indicates that what is in the parentheses is to be treated as a single entity. You need to compute what is in the parentheses first. Also, you can insert parentheses to make sure the expressions you write reflect the order of operations you intend. Review what exponential notation means using examples like: $3^2 = 3 \times 3$, $2^3 = 2 \times 2 \times 2$ and $2^4 = 2 \times 2 \times 2 \times 2$.

Think-Pair-Share is a good classroom arrangement for this problem.

Materials
- Transparencies 4.1A, 4.1B
- Transparency markers

Vocabulary
- order of operations

Explore

Ask students to say in words how the mathematical sentences they write or have to interpret should be computed.

For Question C, suggest they use the order of operations rules to find an answer. Then think about which operation can make an answer greater.

When most students have completed at least one problem in Question C, begin the whole-class summary.

Summarize

Go over Question A and use the discussion to summarize the strategies students have used to help them both write and interpret mathematical sentences. Have students say in words how the expressions should be computed.

Question B provides practice in using the rules for the order of operations.

For Question C, ask students to share strategies that helped them use parentheses to make answers less and strategies that helped make answers greater.

Materials
- Student notebooks

continued on next page

Question D is a challenge because of its length and complexity. If all students have not started this problem, give them a few minutes now to work on it before discussing it.

Have students display their thinking and discuss the problem in steps so that students can reason through and apply the order of operations when the string of symbols is long.

Check for Understanding

For each example, tell the sequence of computations needed to get the correct answer and give the answer.

1. $2^2 + 7 \times (-3) - 5$

2. $(2^2 + 7) \times (-3) - 5$

3. $(2^2 + 7) \times (-3 - 5)$

ACE Assignment Guide
for Problem 4.1

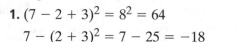

Core 2, 8–16
Other *Applications* 1, *Connections* 17–29, *Extensions* 36–43

Adapted For suggestions about ACE exercises, see the CMP *Special Needs Handbook*.
Connecting to Prior Units 27: *Data About Us*, 29: *Variables and Patterns*

Answers to Problem 4.1

A. 1. Sarah is correct. The correct sequence of computations is -6×4, which gives -24. Then subtract -24 from 5, which gives 29. Then add -3 to get 26.

2. $-3 - (-6) + 5^4 = 3 + 5^4 = 628$

3. $[-3 - (-6) + 5]^4 = 4{,}096$

B. 1. -24 **2.** 149

3. -111.2 **4.** -5

5. -48 **6.** -23

C. The greatest and least values for each are:

1. $(7 - 2 + 3)^2 = 8^2 = 64$
$7 - (2 + 3)^2 = 7 - 25 = -18$

2. $(46 + 2.8) \times 7 - 2 = 339.6$
$46 + 2.8 \times (7 - 2) = 60$

3. $25 \times (-3.12 + 21.3) \div 3 = 151.5$
$[25 \times (-3.12)] + (21.3 \div 3) = -70.9$

4. $5.67 + 35.4 - (178 - 181) = 44.07$
$5.67 + 35.4 - 178 - 181 = -317.03$

D. $3 + 4 \times 5 \div 2 \times 3 - 7^2 + 6 \div 3 = -14$;
$7^2 = 49$; $4 \times 5 = 20$; $20 \div 2 = 10$; $10 \times 3 = 30$;
$6 \div 3 = 2$; $3 + 30 - 49 + 2 = -14$

4.2 Distributing Operations

Goals

- Model the Distributive Property with areas of rectangles that have edges subdivided

- Develop and use the Distributive Property of multiplication over addition

The Distributive Property is very important to students' success in algebra. We introduce it here in a number context and will return to it in the algebra units. We have two kinds of problems to help students make sense of the Distributive Property. Contextualized problems (representing areas of rectangles) let students practice expressing the computations in the language of the situation. Number contexts let students focus on the mechanics of the Distributive Property. Even in these number situations, it is important to continue to ask students to say in words what the computations on each side of the Distributive Property mean and to suggest that students draw rectangle models if they need help in thinking about a problem.

Launch 4.2

Draw a picture of a 6 meter × 10 meter rectangle on the board. Indicate that this represents the area of a back yard where the landowner has marked off a garden across the 10-meter side that is 2 meters long.

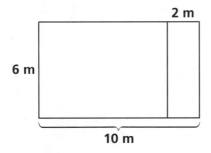

Suggested Questions Solicit student ideas for the following questions and notate what they say.

- *What is the area of the entire backyard?* (6 m × 10 m = 60 m^2)

- *What is the area of the garden?* (6 m × 2 m = 12 m^2)

- *What is the area of the remaining backyard without the garden?* (6 m × 8 m = 48 m^2)

- *How do these parts relate?* (whole yard = garden + rest; so 6 × 10 = (6 × 2) + (6 × 8). Have the class check this statement.)

- *Which is easier to compute: 6 × 10 or (6 × 2) + (6 × 8)?* (6 × 10)

- *Why would you write (6 × 2) + (6 × 8)?* (to show the area of the two sections)

- *The questions you will answer in this problem are like the problem you just analyzed. You will be trying to find expressions for the area of a rectangle and its parts that make computing or subdividing the area easy.*

If your class period is not a full hour, assign and summarize Questions A–D in class. Then assign Question E as homework to be discussed the next class day.

Have students work in small groups on this problem.

Explore 4.2

Continue to ask students to say in words what the sequence of the computations is in each of the number sentences they write.

Try to visit each group for some part of Question A or B so that you can give help, if needed.

Question C asks students to draw rectangle models for given expressions. This is asking the reverse of Questions A and B but uses what is learned in A and B.

Suggested Questions If students are struggling with Question C, ask:

- *What are the dimensions of the needed rectangle?* (7 by 20)

- *How do you show that one side is divided?* (Partition the side into 11 and 9.)

Summarize 4.2

Discuss each of the parts with your students. Look carefully at the rectangle model and make sure they understand how this model can support their thinking. You can help some students by sketching the models on the board or overhead and writing the areas on each of the sections. Some students may remember Tupelo Township from *Bits and Pieces II* in grade 6 and see that this problem is also about finding areas that make up the entire area. The difference is that here we are dealing with measures of the dimensions of parts and their areas rather than relating a fractional part to one whole.

The goal of the problem is, however, to help students to see that the Distributive Property makes sense, can make computation easier, and can help with interpretation in a context.

For Question D, if students struggle, replace the *x* with a box or with a number; work through the problem and then replace the box or the number with an *x*.

Suggested Question

- *What do these problems show us about computing the area of rectangles?* (You can compute the area of the whole rectangle. OR You can compute the areas of all the sections and add them together.)

Note that we do not take the next step to partition each side of a rectangle into two parts with *x* or a multiple of *x* as a part of each edge. This leads to multiplying binomials with variables. This is done in *Frogs, Fleas, and Painted Cubes* in grade 8. However, if your class is interested, use the following Going Further.

Going Further

- *Draw a diagram (rectangular model) to represent the following number sentences:*
$$5(3 + 6) = 5(3) + 5(6)$$
$$3\tfrac{1}{2}(2 + 6) = 3\tfrac{1}{2}(2) + 3\tfrac{1}{2}(6)$$

- *What is the total area of each rectangle?*

- *Write expressions to show two different ways to represent the area of the rectangle below.*

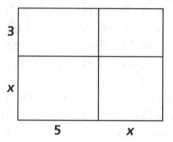

$((3 + x)(5 + x) = (3 \times 5) + (3 \times x)$
$+ (x \times 5) + (x \times x) = 15 + 3x + 5x + x^2 =$
$15 + 8x + x^2)$

4.2 Distributing Operations

Mathematical Goals

- Model the Distributive Property with areas of rectangles that have edges subdivided
- Develop and use the Distributive Property of multiplication over addition

Launch

Draw a picture of a 6 meter × 10 meter rectangle on the board. Indicate that this represents the area of a back yard where the landowner has marked off a garden across the 10-meter side that is 2 meters long.

- *What is the area of the entire back yard?*
- *What is the area of the garden?*
- *What is the area of the remaining yard without the garden?*
- *How do these parts relate?*
- *Which is easier to compute: 6 × 10 or (6 × 2) + (6 × 8)?*
- *Why would you write (6 × 2) + (6 × 8)?*
- *The questions you will answer in this problem are like the problem you just analyzed. You will be trying to find expressions for the area of a rectangle and its parts that make computing or subdividing the area easy.*

If your class period is not a full hour, assign and summarize Questions A–D in class. Assign Question E as homework and discuss it the next class day.

Have students work in small groups on this problem.

Materials
- Transparencies 4.2A, 4.2B

Explore

Continue to ask students to say in words what the sequence of the computations is in each of the number sentences they write.

Try to visit each group for some part of Question A or B so that you can give help, if needed.

Question C asks the reverse of Questions A and B but uses what is learned in Questions A and B. If students are struggling with Question C, ask:

- *What are the dimensions of the needed rectangle?*
- *How do you show that one side is divided?*

Summarize

Discuss each of the parts with your students. Look carefully at the rectangle model and make sure they understand how this model can support their thinking. Have students sketch the models on the board or overhead and write the areas on each of the sections.

Materials
- Student notebooks

continued on next page

Summarize
continued

For Question D, if students struggle, replace the *x* with a box or a number; work through the problem, then replace the box or the number with an *x*.

- *What do these problems show us about computing the area of rectangles?*

Going Further

- *Write expressions to show two different ways to represent the area of this rectangle. (Draw a rectangle with the dimensions: 3 + x by 5 + x.)*

ACE Assignment Guide for Problem 4.2

Core 4

Other *Applications* 3, *Connections* 30–32, *Extensions* 44; unassigned choices from previous problems

Adapted For suggestions about adapting Exercise 4 and other ACE exercises, see the CMP *Special Needs Handbook*.

Connecting to Prior Units 30: *Bits and Pieces I*, 32: *Variables and Patterns*

Answers to Problem 4.2

A. 1. 6,000 yd^2

   2. a. The areas are 3,600 yd^2 and 2,400 yd^2.

     b. $(30 \times 120) + (20 \times 120) =$
$(20 + 30) \times 120 = 50 \times 120 = 6{,}000$ yd^2

   3. a. $(30 \times 80) = 2{,}400$ yd^2;
$(20 \times 80) = 1{,}600$ yd^2;
$(30 \times 40) = 1{,}200$ yd^2;
$(20 \times 40) = 800$ yd^2;

     b. $(30 \times 80) + (20 \times 80) + (30 \times 40)$
$+ (20 \times 40) = (30 + 20) \times (80 + 40) =$
$6{,}000$ yd^2

B. 1. $12 \times (3 + 7)$ or $(12 \times 3) + (12 \times 7)$; the first requires one fewer step.

   2. $(4 + 8) \times (3 + 7)$ or $(4 \times 3) + (4 \times 7)$
$+ (8 \times 3) + (8 \times 7)$; the first

   3. $(3 + 2) \times (17 + 4)$ or $(3 \times 17) + (3 \times 4)$
$+ (2 \times 17) + (2 \times 4)$; the first

   4. $5 \times (17 + 4)$ or $(5 \times 17) + (5 \times 4)$; the first

C. 1.

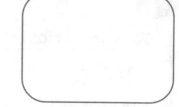

   2. $(7 \times 11) + (7 \times 9)$

   3.

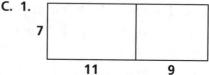

   4. $4 \times (3 + 4)$ or
$(3 \times 3) + (3 \times 4) + (1 \times 3) + (1 \times 4)$

D. 1. $8x$

   2. a. $(3 + 2) \times x$ or $3x + 2x$

     b. $(5 + x) \times 1.5$ or $(5 \times 1.5) + (x \times 1.5)$

E. 1. $12 \times (6 + 4) = (12 \times \mathbf{6}) + (12 \times \mathbf{4})$

   2. $2 \times (n + 4) = (2 \times \mathbf{n}) + (\mathbf{2} \times 4)$

   3. $(n \times 5) + (n \times 3) = \mathbf{n} \cdot (5 + 3)$

   4. $(-3 \times 5) + (-3 \times 7) = -3 \cdot (\mathbf{5} + 7)$

   5. $4n + 11n = n \cdot (\mathbf{4 + 11})$

4.3 The Distributive Property and Subtraction

Goals

- Develop and use the Distributive Property of multiplication over subtraction
- Use the Distributive Property to solve problems

In this problem, we name the Distributive Property that students explored in Problem 4.2 and raise the issue of whether the Distributive Property works with subtraction.

Launch 4.3

Use the Getting Ready to review and summarize the Distributive Property for multiplication and addition. Problem 1 in the Getting Ready looks at the Distributive Property used to *expand* an expression. Problem 2 looks at using the Distributive Property in the other direction, to *factor* an expression. You can relate factoring to writing the expression as a product of factors (one or both of which might have two terms) and expanding the expression to writing the expression as a sum of addends (one or both of which might be products).

When you feel that the class is making sense of the Distributive Property, raise the issue of whether the property would hold if the operations were multiplication and subtraction, rather than multiplication and addition.

Suggested Questions You can ask questions such as the following and get an idea or two from the class, but leave the questions as things students should ask themselves as they work on the problem.

- *Do you think the Distributive Property can be used to expand or factor an expression with subtraction? Why or why not?*
- *Can you give an example?*
- *When you have a subtraction expression, can you use integers to write the expression as an addition expression?*

Have students work in pairs.

Explore 4.3

If students are having trouble with subtraction, give them a simple problem like $2 - 3$, and ask them to write an addition problem with the same answer. They should see that $2 - 3 = 2 + (-3)$. Also look at $2 - (-3)$ and write it as $2 + 3$. This should give some support to students having trouble.

Also suggest that they apply the Distributive Property and check to see if the two forms for the expressions give the same answers.

Suggested Questions

- *What would the expression $-5 \times (3 - 2)$ look like if you expanded it using the Distributive Property?* [$(-5 \times 3) - (-5 \times 2)$]
- *Does this give the same answer as the original expression if you compute it?* (Yes, they are both equal to -5.)
- *Suppose you write the original expression using adding the opposite. How would the expression look?* [$-5 \times (3 + (-2))$; this also equals -5.]

Summarize 4.3

Have students report on Questions A–C. These are purely number problems that give practice with using the Distributive Property to expand and factor expressions with addition or subtraction.

Suggested Questions Continue to ask questions like:

- *How are addition and subtraction related?* (They are the inverse of each other.)
- *Give an example where this idea is useful.* (You can rewrite an expression with subtraction as an expression with addition by remembering that subtracting and adding the opposite give you the same answer. So, $-7 \times [-4 - (-6)]$ is equivalent to $-7 \times (-4 + 6)$. This is true because subtracting -6 is the same as adding the opposite of -6, which is 6.)
- *How can you tell factored form from expanded form?* (Factored form is the product of two factors, and expanded form is the sum or difference of two expressions.)

INVESTIGATION 4

Investigation 4 Properties of Operations   **95**

- *Which form seems the most useful for computing, expanded or factored form?* (Factored form has fewer steps when computing.)

- *In* $-5 \times (3 + 2)$, *how can you tell* -5 *and* $(3 + 2)$ *are factors?* (The parentheses indicate that $(3 + 2)$ should be thought of as one number. You could put a box or an *x* in its place and see the two factors. So, this is a product of two numbers, one of which is a sum of two numbers!)

- *Explain how you can use the Distributive Property to expand an expression that is the product of two factors where one is a sum (or difference) of two numbers.* (Multiply the first factor by each number in the second factor. For example, $-5 \times [3 + (-2)] = (-5 \times 3) + [-5 \times (-2)] = -15 + 10 = -5$.)

- *Explain how you can use the Distributive Property to factor an expression that is the sum of two terms with a common factor.* [Identify a common factor for the two terms. Then write the expressions as the product of the common factor and another factor that is the sum of two terms gotten by dividing each of the original expressions by the common term. For example, $-6 \cdot 2 + (-6) \cdot 3$ is made up of two terms which have a common factor of -6. You can write the original expression as the common factor -6 multiplied by the sum of the two terms with the common factor divided out, or $-6 \cdot (2 + 3)$].

Questions D and E are very important. They are real-life contexts that show the usefulness of the Distributive Property. Call on more than one student to present a solution and to describe their strategy for solving the problem. Question E part (3) is a classic dilemma for many adults.

Review the notes on notation with students.

Check for Understanding

- *Calculate the following:*
  $$4 + 3(6 + 8) - 10$$
  $$4 - 3(6 + 8) - 10$$
  $$4 - 3(6 - 8) - 10$$

(**Note:** Students can apply the distributive property first and then the order of operations or they can just apply the order of operations.)

4.3 The Distributive Property and Subtraction

Mathematical Goals

- Develop and use the Distributive Property of multiplication over subtraction
- Use the Distributive Property to solve problems

Launch

Use the Getting Ready to review and summarize the Distributive Property for multiplication and addition. Relate factoring to writing the expression as a product of factors and expanding the expression to writing the expression as a sum of addends.

Raise the issue of whether the property would hold if the operations were multiplication and subtraction. Leave the questions for students to ask themselves as they work on the problem.

- *Do you think the Distributive Property can be used to expand or factor an expression with subtraction? Why or why not?*
- *Can you give an example?*
- *When you have a subtraction expression, can you use integers to write the expression as an addition expression?*

Have students work in pairs.

Materials
- Transparency 4.3
- Transparency markers

Vocabulary
- Distributive Property

Explore

If students are having trouble with subtraction, give them a simple problem like $2 - 3$, and ask them to write an addition problem with the same answer.

Also suggest that they apply the Distributive Property and check to see if the two forms for the expressions give the same answers.

- *What would the expression $-5 \times (3 - 2)$ look like if you expanded it using the Distributive Property?*
- *Does this give the same answer as the original expression?*

Summarize

Have students report on Questions A–C. Continue to ask questions like:

- *How are addition and subtraction related?*
- *Give an example where this idea is useful.*
- *How can you tell factored form from expanded form?*
- *Which form seems the most useful for computing, expanded or factored form?*
- *In $-5 \times (3 + 2)$, how can you tell that -5 and $(3 + 2)$ are factors?*

Materials
- Student notebooks

continued on next page

Summarize
continued

- *Explain how you can use the Distributive Property to expand an expression that is the product of two factors where one is a sum (or difference) of two numbers.*

- *Explain how you can use the Distributive Property to factor an expression that is the sum of two terms with a common factor.*

Questions D and E are very important. Call on more than one student to present a solution and to describe their strategy for solving the problem.

Review the notes on notation with students.

ACE Assignment Guide for Problem 4.3

Core 6
Other *Applications* 5, 7; *Connections* 33–35; *Extensions* 45, 46; unassigned choices from previous problems

Adapted For suggestions about adapting Exercise 6 and other ACE exercises, see the CMP *Special Needs Handbook*.
Connecting to Prior Units 34: *Bits and Pieces III*

Answers to Problem 4.3

A. 1. $(5 \cdot 3) + (5 \cdot 2)$
   2. $(5 \cdot 3) + [5 \cdot (-2)]$
   3. $(5 \cdot 3) - (5 \cdot 2)$
   4. $(5 \cdot 3) - [5 \cdot (-2)]$
   5. 25; 5; 5; 25
   6. Yes. It works the same as for addition. You just have a different sign between the two terms.

B. 1. $(-5 \cdot 3) + (-5 \cdot 2)$
   2. $(-5 \cdot 3) - (-5 \cdot 2)$
   3. $(-5 \cdot 3) + [-5 \cdot (-2)]$
   4. $(-5 \cdot 3) - [-5 \cdot (-2)]$
   5. $-25; -5; -5; -25$
   6. Multiply the negative number by each term in the second factor, just as you do for addition.

C. 1. $6 \cdot (2 + 3)$
   2. $6 \cdot (2 - 3)$
   3. $-6 \cdot (2 + 3)$
   4. $-6 \cdot (2 - 3)$
   5. $(5 - 8) \cdot x$
   6. $(-3 - 4) \cdot x$
   7. Identify the factor (positive or negative) that each term has in common. Rewrite the expression as the product of the common factor (whether it is positive or negative) times the sum or difference of the terms with the common factor removed.

D. 1. Yes. She has 15 items, so she makes it, but just barely.
   2. $3 \cdot (2 + 3)$ or $(3 \times 2) + (3 \times 3)$
   3. $(3 \times 2) + (3 \times 3)$ or $3 \cdot (2 + 3)$

E. 1. $4.0352 or $4.04
   2. $(\$1.19 + \$2.69) \cdot 1.04$ or $1.04 \cdot \$1.19 + 1.04 \cdot \$2.69$
   3. It is just the Distributive Property, so either method works. There are fewer steps when you add and then multiply.

The student edition pages for this
investigation begin on the next page.

Notes _____
_____
_____
_____

Properties of Operations

When you learn new types of numbers, you want to know what properties apply to them. You know that rational numbers are commutative for addition and multiplication.

$$-\frac{2}{3} + \frac{1}{6} = \frac{1}{6} + \left(-\frac{2}{3}\right) \text{ and } -\frac{2}{3} \times \frac{1}{6} = \frac{1}{6} \times \left(-\frac{2}{3}\right)$$

In this investigation, you will study another important property of rational numbers. You will also learn a mathematical rule that tells you the order in which to do arithmetic operations.

4.1 Order of Operations

Mathematicians have established rules called the **order of operations** in which to perform operations $(+, -, \times, \div)$. Why do you need such rules?

Rules make this clear:
6 + 20 · 5

60   Accentuate the Negative

Notes _____

_____

_____

_____

The rugby club orders 20 new jerseys. The manufacturer charges a $100 setup fee and $15 per shirt. The total cost is represented by the equation, $C = 100 + 15n$, where C is the cost in dollars and n is the number of jerseys ordered. Pedro and David calculate the amount the club owes.

Pedro's calculation: $C = 100 + 15 \times 20$

                                  $= 100 + 300$

                                  $= \$400$

David's calculation: $C = 100 + 15 \times 20$

                                  $= 115 \times 20$

                                  $= \$2,300$

- Who did the calculations correctly?

Notes _____

_____

_____

_____

Order of Operations

1. Compute any expressions within parentheses.

Example 1

$(-7 - 2) + 1 =$

$-9 + 1 = -8$

Example 2

$(1 + 2) \times (-4) =$

$3 \times (-4) = -12$

2. Compute any exponents.

Example 1

$-2 + 3^2 =$

$-2 + 9 = 7$

Example 2

$6 - (-1 + 4)^2 =$

$6 - (3)^2 = -3$

3. Multiply and divide in order from left to right.

Example 1

$1 + 2 \times 4 =$ Multiplication first

$1 + 8 = 9$

Example 2

$200 \div 10 \times 2 =$ Division first

$20 \times 2 = 40$ Multiplication second

4. Add and subtract in order from left to right.

$1 + 2 - 3 \times 4 =$ Multiplication first

$1 + 2 - 12 =$ Addition and subtraction

$3 - 12 = -9$

Notes

Use the order of operations in Problem 4.1.

A. In a game, the goal is to write a number sentence that gives the greatest possible result using all the numbers on four cards. Jeremy draws the following four cards.

1. Joshua writes $5 - (-6) \times 4 + (-3) = 41$. Sarah says the result should be 26. Who is correct and why?
2. Wendy starts by writing $-3 - (-6) + 5^4 =$. What is her result?
3. Insert parentheses into $-3 - (-6) + 5^4$ to give a greater result than in part (2).

B. Find each value.

1. $-7 \times 4 + 8 \div 2$
2. $(3 + 2)^2 \times 6 - 1$
3. $2\frac{2}{5} \times 4\frac{1}{2} - 5^3 + 3$
4. $8 \times (4 - 5)^3 + 3$
5. $-8 \times [4 - (-5 + 3)]$
6. $-16 \div 8 \times 2^3 + (-7)$

C. Use parentheses, if needed, to make the greatest and least possible values.

1. $7 - 2 + 3^2$
2. $46 + 2.8 \times 7 - 2$
3. $25 \times (-3.12) + 21.3 \div 3$
4. $5.67 + 35.4 - 178 - 181$

D. Use the order of operations to solve this problem. Show your work.

$$3 + 4 \times 5 \div 2 \times 3 - 7^2 + 6 \div 3 = \blacksquare$$

ACE Homework starts on page 69.

Investigation 4 Properties of Operations **63**

Notes _____

_____

_____

_____

4.2 Distributing Operations

In this problem, you will compute areas of rectangles using different expressions. Look for ways to rewrite an expression into an equivalent expression that is easier to compute.

Problem **4.2** Distributing Operations

A. Richard lives in a neighborhood with a rectangular field. Each part below shows a way to divide the field for different kinds of sports.

1. Find the area.

50 yds

120 yds

2. The field is divided into two parts.

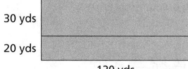

30 yds

20 yds

120 yds

  a. Find the area of each part.

  b. Write a number sentence that shows that the sum of the smaller areas is equal to the area of the entire field.

3. The field is divided into four parts.

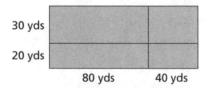

30 yds

20 yds

80 yds   40 yds

  a. Find the area of each part.

  b. Write a number sentence that shows that the sum of the smaller areas is equal to the area of the entire field.

STUDENT PAGE

Notes _____

_____

_____

_____

B. Use what you learned in Question A. Write two different expressions to find the area of each rectangle. Tell which uses fewer operations.

1.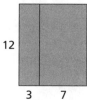

2.

3.

4.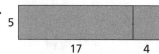

C. **1.** Draw a rectangle whose area can be represented by $7 \times (11 + 9)$.

  2. Write another expression for the area of the rectangle in part (1).

  3. Draw a rectangle whose area can be represented by $(3 + 1) \times (3 + 4)$.

  4. Write another expression for the area of the rectangle in part (3).

D. The unknown length in each rectangle is represented by a variable x.

  1. Write an expression to represent the area of the rectangle.

  2. Write two different expressions to represent the area of each rectangle below.

  a.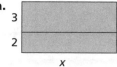

  b.

E. Find the missing part(s) to make each sentence true.

  1. $12 \times (6 + 4) = (12 \times \blacksquare) + (12 \times 4)$

  2. $2 \times (n + 4) = (2 \times \blacksquare) + (\blacksquare \times 4)$

  3. $(n \times 5) + (n \times 3) = \blacksquare \cdot (5 + 3)$

  4. $(-3 \times 5) + (\blacksquare \times 7) = -3 \cdot (\blacksquare + 7)$

  5. $4n + 11n = n \cdot (\blacksquare + \blacksquare)$

ACE **Homework starts on page 69.**

Notes _____

_____

_____

_____

The Distributive Property and Subtraction

The rectangles in Problem 4.2 illustrate an important property of numbers and operations called the **Distributive Property.** This property shows that multiplication *distributes* over addition. When you think about a multiplication problem like 512×5 as $500 \times 5 + 12 \times 5$, or $12 \times 5\frac{3}{4}$ as $12 \times 5 + 12 \times \frac{3}{4}$, you are using the Distributive Property.

Getting Ready for Problem

You can use the Distributive Property to rewrite an expression as one that is easier to calculate or gives new information. You can do this in two ways.

1. Suppose an expression is written as the product of two factors, one of which is a sum. You can use the Distributive Property to multiply one factor by each number in the second factor. This is called *expanding* the expression.

$$-3 \cdot (4 + 8) = -3 \cdot 4 + (-3) \cdot 8$$

With a variable: $-2 \cdot (x + 6) = -2x + (-2) \cdot 6$

2. Suppose an expression is written as a sum and the numbers have a common factor. You can use the Distributive Property to rewrite the expression as the common factor multiplied by the sum. This is called *factoring* the expression.

$$5 \cdot 4 + 5 \cdot 7 = 5 \cdot (4 + 7)$$

With a variable: $8 \cdot 2 + 8x = 8 \cdot (2 + x)$

• Do you think the Distributive Property can be used to expand or factor expressions with subtraction? Explain your reasoning.

Notes

Problem 4.3 The Distributive Property and Subtraction

A. Use the Distributive Property to expand each expression.

1. $5 \cdot (3 + 2)$ **2.** $5 \cdot [3 + (-2)]$

3. $5 \cdot (3 - 2)$ **4.** $5 \cdot [3 - (-2)]$

5. For parts (1)–(4), find the value of the expression.

6. Does the Distributive Property seem to hold for subtraction? Explain.

B. Use the Distributive Property to expand each expression.

1. $-5 \cdot (3 + 2)$ **2.** $-5 \cdot (3 - 2)$

3. $-5 \cdot [3 + (-2)]$ **4.** $-5 \cdot [3 - (-2)]$

5. For parts (1)–(4), find the value of the expression.

6. Explain how to distribute a negative number to expand an expression.

C. Write each expression in factored form.

1. $6 \cdot 2 + 6 \cdot 3$ **2.** $6 \cdot 2 - 6 \cdot 3$

3. $-6 \cdot 2 + (-6) \cdot 3$ **4.** $-6 \cdot 2 - (-6) \cdot 3$

5. $5x - 8x$ **6.** $-3x - 4x$

7. Explain how to factor an expression with subtraction.

D. Three friends are going hiking. Lisa buys 2 bottles of water and 3 packs of trail mix for each of them.

1. Can she go through the express checkout lane for customers with 15 or fewer items?

2. Write a number sentence to show how you found the total number of items.

3. Write another number sentence to find the total number of items.

E. Mr. Chan bought a roll of kitchen towels for $1.19 and window cleaner for $2.69. In his state there is a 4% sales tax on these items.

1. What is his total bill?

2. Write a number sentence to show how you found the total bill.

3. Suppose you add the prices of the two items and then compute the tax. Your friend finds the tax on each item and then adds the two together. Which method is better? Explain.

ACE **Homework starts on page 69.**

Investigation 4 Properties of Operations   **67**

STUDENT PAGE

STUDENT PAGE

Notes _____

_____

_____

_____

(67) 98

More on Notation

Now you can use the order of operations or the Distributive Property to find the value of an expression like $-8 \cdot [-2 + (-3)]$ that has parentheses.

Order of operations method:

$$-8 \cdot [-2 + (-3)] = -8 \cdot (-5) \qquad \text{Add } -2 \text{ and } -3 \text{ within the parentheses.}$$
$$= 40 \qquad \text{Multiply.}$$

Distributive Property method:

$$-8 \cdot [-2 + (-3)] = -8 \cdot (-2) + (-8) \cdot (-3) \qquad \text{Expand first.}$$
$$= 16 + 24 \qquad \text{Multiply.}$$
$$= 40$$

Either method is correct.

Notes _____

_____

_____

_____

Applications

1. Find the values of each pair of expressions.

   a. $-12 + (-4 + 9)$ $[-12 + (-4)] + 9$

   b. $(14 - 20) - 2^3$ $14 - (20 - 2^3)$

   c. $[14 + (-20)] + -8$ $14 + [-20 + (-8)]$

   d. $-1 - [-1 + (-1)]$ $[-1 - (-1)] + (-1)$

   e. Which cases lead to expressions with different results? Explain.

2. Find the value of each expression.

   a. $(5 - 3) \div (-2) \times (-1)$ **b.** $2 + (-3) \times 4 - (-5)$

   c. $4 \times 2 \times (-3) + (-10) \div 5$ **d.** $-3 \times [2 + (-10)] - 2^2$

   e. $(4 - 20) \div 2^2 - 5 \times (-2)$ **f.** $10 - [50 \div (-2 \times 25) - 7] \times 2^2$

3. Draw and label the edges and areas of a rectangle to illustrate each pair of equivalent expressions.

   For: Help with Exercise 3
   Web Code: ane-4403

   a. $(3 + 2) \cdot 12 = 3 \cdot 12 + 2 \cdot 12$

   b. $9 \cdot 3 + 9 \cdot 5 = 9 \cdot (3 + 5)$

   c. $x \cdot (5 + 9) = 5x + 9x$

   d. $2 \cdot (x + 8) = 2x + 16$

4. Write equivalent expressions to show two different ways to find the area of each rectangle. Use the ideas of the Distributive Property.

   a.

   b.

   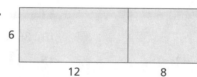

   c.

   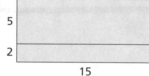

   d.

   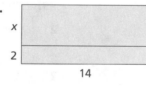
   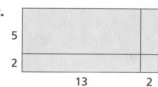

Notes _____

_____

_____

_____

5. Rewrite each expression in an equivalent form to show a simpler way to do the arithmetic. Explain how you know the two results are equal without doing any calculations.

  a. $(-150 + 270) + 30$

  b. $(43 \times 120) + [43 \times (-20)]$

  c. $23 + (-75) + 14 + (-23) - (-75)$

  d. $(0.8 \times -23) + (0.8 \times -7)$

6. Without doing any calculations, determine whether each number sentence is true. Explain. Then check your answer.

  a. $50 \times 432 = (50 \times 400) + (50 \times 32)$

  b. $50 \times 368 = (50 \times 400) - (50 \times 32)$

  c. $-50 \times (-800) = (-50 \times (-1{,}000)) + (-50 \times 200)$

  d. $-50 + (400 \times 32) = (-50 + 400) \times (-50 + 32)$

  e. $(-70 \times 20) + (-50 \times 20) = (-120) \times 20$

  f. $6 \times 17 = 6 \times 20 - 6 \times 3$

7. For each part, use the Distributive Property to write an equivalent expression.

  a. $-2 \times [5 + (-8)]$ b. $(-3 \cdot 2) - [-3 \cdot (-12)]$

  c. $x \cdot (-3 + 5)$ d. $(-7x) + (4x)$

  e. $2x \cdot [2 - (-4)]$ f. $(x) - (3x)$

Connections

Find the sum, difference, product, or quotient.

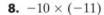

8. $-10 \times (-11)$ 9. -10×11

10. $10 - 11$ 11. $-3 \div (-12)$

12. $3^2 \times 2^2$ 13. $3^2 \times (-2)^2$

14. $-24 - (-12)$ 15. $\dfrac{-24}{-12}$

16. $-48 \div 4^2$ 17. 50×70

18. $50 \times (-70)$ 19. $2{,}200 \div (-22)$

20. $-50 \times (-120)$ 21. $-139 + 899$

22. $5{,}600 - 7{,}800$ 23. $-4{,}400 - (-1{,}200)$

24. $\dfrac{-9{,}900}{-99}$ 25. $-580 + (-320)$

STUDENT PAGE

Notes _____

_____

_____

_____

26. When using negative numbers and exponents, parentheses are sometimes needed to make it clear what you are multiplying.

-5^4 can be thought of as "the opposite of 5^4" or $-(5^4) = -(5 \cdot 5 \cdot 5 \cdot 5) = -625$

$(-5)^4$ can be thought of as "negative five to the fourth power" or $-5 \cdot (-5) \cdot (-5) \cdot (-5) = 625$

Indicate whether each expression will be negative or positive.

a. -3^2 **b.** $(-6)^3$ **c.** $(-4)^4$ **d.** -1^6 **e.** $(-3)^4$

27. The following list shows the yards gained and lost on each play by the Mathville Mudhens in the fourth quarter of their last football game:

$$-8, 20, 3, 7, -15, 4, -12, 32, 5, 1$$

Write an expression that shows how to compute their average gain or loss per play. Then compute the average.

28. Complete each number sentence.

a. $-34 + (-15) = \blacksquare$ **b.** $-12 \times (-23) = \blacksquare$

c. $-532 \div (-7) = \blacksquare$ **d.** $-777 - (-37) = \blacksquare$

e. Write a fact family for part (a).   **f.** Write a fact family for part (b).

29. Write a related fact. Use it to find the value of n that makes the sentence true.

a. $n - (-5) = 35$ **b.** $4 + n = -43$

c. $-2n = -16$ **d.** $\frac{n}{4} = -32$

Investigation 4 Properties of Operations   **71**

Notes _____
_____
_____
_____

30. Multiple Choice Which set of numbers is in order from least to greatest?

A. 31.4, -14.2, $-55, 75$, -0.05, 0.5, 3.140

B. $\frac{2}{5}$, $\frac{-3}{5}$, $\frac{8}{7}$, $\frac{-9}{8}$, $\frac{-3}{2}$, $\frac{5}{3}$

C. -0.2, -0.5, 0.75, 0.6, -1, 1.5

D. None of these

31. Find the absolute values of the numbers for each set in Exercise 30. Write them in order from least to greatest.

32. A trucking company carries freight along a highway from New York City to San Francisco. Its home base is in Omaha, Nebraska, which is about halfway between the two cities. Truckers average about 50 miles per hour on this route.

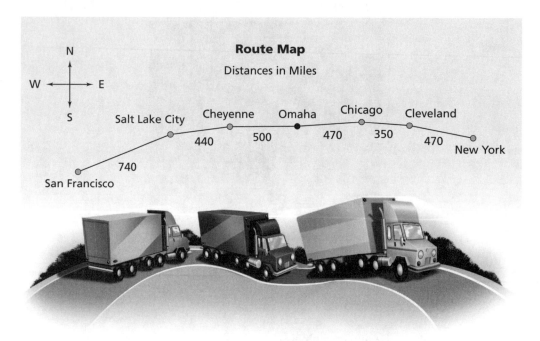

Make a number line to represent this truck route. Put Omaha at 0. Use positive numbers for cities east of Omaha and negative numbers for cities west of Omaha. Then write number sentences to answer each question.

a. A truck leaves Omaha heading east and travels for 7 hours. About how far does the truck go? Where on the number line does it stop?

Notes _____

_____

_____

_____

b. A truck leaves Omaha heading west and travels for 4.5 hours. About how far does the truck go? Where on the number line does it stop?

c. A truck heading east arrives in Omaha. About where on the number line was the truck 12 hours earlier?

d. A truck heading west arrives in Omaha. About where on the number line was the truck 11 hours earlier?

33. Insert parentheses (or brackets) in each expression where needed to show how to get each result.

  a. $1 + (-3) \times (-4) = 8$ **b.** $1 + (-3) \times (-4) = 13$

  c. $-6 \div (-2) + (-4) = 1$ **d.** $-6 \div (-2) + (-4) = -1$

  e. $-4 \times 2 - 10 = -18$ **f.** $-4 \times 2 - 10 = 32$

34. A grocery store receipt shows 5% state tax due on laundry detergent and a flower bouquet.

| Laundry Detergent | $7.99 | T |
| Flower Bouquet | $3.99 | T |

Does it matter whether the tax is calculated on each separate item or the total cost? Explain.

35. You can use dot patterns to illustrate distributive properties for operations on whole numbers. Write a number sentence to represent the pair of dot patterns.

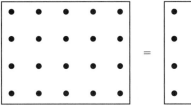 =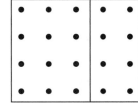

Investigation 4 Properties of Operations   **73**

Notes _____

_____

_____

_____

Extensions

Copy each pair of expressions in Exercises 36–40. Insert < or > to make a true statement.

36. -23 ■ -45

37. $-23 + 10$ ■ $-45 + 10$

38. $-23 - 10$ ■ $-45 - 10$

39. -23×10 ■ -45×10

40. $-23 \times (-10)$ ■ $-45 \times (-10)$

Based on your results in Exercises 36–40, complete each statement. Test your ideas with other numerical cases, or develop another kind of explanation, perhaps using chip board or number line ideas.

41. If $a > b$, then $a + c$ ■ $b + c$.

42. If $a > b$, then $a - c$ ■ $b - c$.

43. If $a > b$, then $a \times c$ ■ $b \times c$.

44. Find the value for n that makes the sentence true.

    a. $n - (-24) = 12$ **b.** $2.5n = -10$ **c.** $2.5n + (-3) = -13$

45. Complete each pair of calculations.

    a. $12 \div (-8 + 4) = $ ■ $[12 \div (-8)] + (12 \div 4) = $ ■

    b. $-12 \div [-5 - (-3)] = $ ■ $[-12 \div (-5)] - [-12 \div (-3)] = $ ■

    c. $4 \div (-2 - 6) = $ ■ $(4 \div -2) - (4 \div 6) = $ ■

    d. $3 \div (5 + 6) = $ ■ $(3 \div 5) + (3 \div 6) = $ ■

    e. What can you conclude from parts (a)–(d) about the Distributive Property?

46. When you find the mean (average) of two numbers, you add them together and divide by 2.

    a. Is the operation of finding the average of two numbers commutative? Give examples.

    b. Does multiplication distribute over the averaging operation? That is, will a number a times the average of two numbers, x and y, give the same thing as the average of ax and ay? Give examples.

Notes _____

_____

_____

_____

Mathematical Reflections 4

In this investigation, you compared important properties of arithmetic with positive numbers to properties of arithmetic with negative numbers. The following questions will help you summarize what you have learned.

Think about your answers. Discuss your ideas with other students and your teacher. Then write a summary of your findings in your notebook.

1. a. What is the order of operations? Why is it important for you to understand?

  b. Give an example of an equation where the use of parentheses changes the result of the computation.

2. a. What does it mean to say that an operation is *commutative?*

  b. Which operations on integers are commutative? Give numerical examples.

3. What does it mean to say that *multiplication distributes over addition* and *subtraction?* Give numerical examples.

Notes _____

_____

_____

_____

Investigation

ACE
Assignment Choices

Differentiated
Instruction
Solutions for All Learners

Problem 4.1

Core 2, 8–16
Other *Applications* 1, *Connections* 17–29,
Extensions 36–43

Problem 4.2

Core 4
Other *Applications* 3, *Connections* 30–32,
Extensions 44; unassigned choices from previous
problems

Problem 4.3

Core 6
Other *Applications* 5, 7; *Connections* 33–35;
Extensions 45, 46; unassigned choices from
previous problems

Adapted For suggestions about adapting
Exercise 4 and other ACE exercises, see the
CMP *Special Needs Handbook*.
Connecting to Prior Units 27: *Data About Us*,
29: *Variables and Patterns*, 30: *Bits and Pieces I*, 32:
Variables and Patterns, 34: *Bits and Pieces III*

Applications

1. **a.** $-12 + (-4 + 9) = -7$
   $-12 + (5) = -7$
   $[-12 + (-4)] + 9 = -7$
   $(-16) + 9 = -7$

   b. $(14 - 20) - 2^3 = -14$
   $(-6) - 8 = -14$
   $14 - (20 - 2^3) = 2$
   $14 - (12) = 2$

   These do not result in the same answer
   because subtraction is not associative
   (Associative Property does not hold), while
   addition is associative.

   c. $[14 + (-20)] + (-8) = -14$
   $(-6) + (-8) = -14$

$14 + [-20 + (-8)] = -14$
$14 + (-28) = -14$

d. $-1 - [-1 + (-1)] = 1$
$-1 - (-2) = 1$

$[-1 - (-1)] + (-1) = -1$
$0 + (-1) = -1$

e. Problems with subtraction lead to different
results. Subtraction cannot be done in any
order. Addition can be done in any order,
so changing the order in parts (a) and (c)
did not change the answer.

2. **a.** 1   **b.** -5 **c.** -26
   d. 20   **e.** 6   **f.** 42

3. **a.**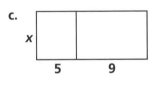
   b.

   c.

   d.

4. **a.** $(5 + 2) \times 15$ or $(5 \times 15) + (2 \times 15)$

   b. $6 \times (12 + 8)$ or $(6 \times 12) + (6 \times 8)$

   c. $(5 + 2) \times (13 + 2)$ or
   $(5 \times 13) + (5 \times 2) + (2 \times 13) + (2 \times 2)$

   d. $(x + 2) \times 14$ or $(x \times 14) + (2 \times 14)$

5. **a.** $(-150 + 270) + 30 = (270 + 30) + (-150) =$
   $300 - 150 = 150$; addition is commutative
   and associative.

   b. $(43 \times 120) + [43 \times (-20)] =$
   $43 \times (120 - 20) = 43 \times (100) = 4,300$;
   Distributive Property of multiplication
   (over addition); $120 + (-20) = 100$

ACE ANSWERS 4

c. $23 + (-75) + 14 + (-23) - (-75) =$
$[23 + (-23)] + [-75 - (-75)] + 14 =$
$(23 - 23) + (-75 + 75) + 14 = 14;$
addition is commutative and associative.

d. $[0.8 \times (-23)] + [0.8 \times (-7)] = 0.8 \times [-23 + (-7)] = 0.8 \times (-30) = -24;$ Distributive Property (of multiplication over addition)

6. a. True. Using the Distributive Property, 432 groups of 50 is the same as 400 groups of 50 plus 32 groups of 50.

b. True. Using the Distributive Property, $400 - 32 = 368$. 400 groups of 50 minus 32 groups of 50 is the same as 368 groups of 50.

c. True. By using the Distributive Property.

d. Not true. The Distributive Property is not applied correctly; multiplication is distributed over addition, not addition distributed over multiplication.

e. True. Distributive Property.
$-70 + (-50) = -120$

f. True. Distributive Property. $20 - 3 = 17$

7. a. $-2 \times [5 + (-8)] = (-2 \times 5) + [-2 \times (-8)]$

b. $(-3 \cdot 2) - [-3 \cdot (-12)] = -3 \cdot [2 - (-12)]$

c. $x \cdot (-3 + 5) = -3x + 5x$

d. $(-7x) + (4x) = x \cdot (-7 + 4)$

e. $2x \cdot [2 - (-4)] = 2 \cdot 2x - (-4) \cdot 2x$

f. $(x) - (3x) = x \cdot (1 - 3)$

Connections

8. $-10 \times (-11) = 110$

9. $-10 \times 11 = -110$

10. $10 - 11 = -1$

11. $-3 \div (-12) = \frac{1}{4}$

12. $3^2 \times 2^2 = 36$ **13.** $3^2 \times (-2)^2 = 36$

14. $-24 - (-12) = -12$

15. $\frac{-24}{-12} = 2$

16. $-48 \div 4^2 = -3$

17. $50 \times 70 = 3,500$

18. $50 \times (-70) = -3,500$

19. $2,200 \div (-22) = -100$

20. $-50 \times (-120) = 6,000$

21. $-139 + 899 = 760$

22. $5,600 - 7,800 = -2,200$

23. $-4,400 - (-1,200) = -3,200$

24. $-9,900 \div (-99) = 100$ **25.** -900

26. a. Negative. The opposite of 3^2 is $-(3^2)$ or -9.

b. Negative. $(-6)^3 = -6 \cdot (-6) \cdot (-6)$ or -216

c. Positive. A negative multiplied an even number of times will result in a positive product.
$(-4)^4 = -4 \cdot (-4) \cdot (-4) \cdot (-4) = 256$

d. Negative. $1^6 = 1$, so $-1^6 = -(1^6)$ or -1

e. Positive. Four negative numbers multiplied together will result in a positive product.
$-3 \cdot (-3) \cdot (-3) \cdot (-3) = 81$

27. $\dfrac{-8 + 20 + 3 + 7 - 15 + 4 - 12 + 32 + 5 + 1}{10} =$
$\frac{37}{10} = 3.7$; a gain of 3.7 yards per play

28. a. $-34 + (-15) = -49$

b. $-12 \times (-23) = 276$

c. $-532 \div (-7) = 76$

d. $-777 - (-37) = -740$

e. $-49 - (-34) = -15; -49 - (-15) = -34;$
$-15 + (-34) = -49$

f. $276 \div (-12) = -23; 276 \div (-23) = -12;$
$-23 \times (-12) = 276$

29. a. $n - (-5) = 35; n = 35 + (-5); 5 = 35 - n;$
answers will vary for the related fact.
$n = 30$. Some students find the "missing addend" problem to be easier to reason, but other students may find one of the other forms easier, such as $n = 35 + (-5)$.

b. $4 + n = -43; n = -43 - 4; 4 = -43 - n;$
$n = -47$

c. $-2n = -16; n = -16 \cdot (-\frac{1}{2}); n = 8$

d. $\frac{n}{4} = -32; n = -32 \cdot (4); n = -128$

30. D

31. A: 0.05, 0.5, 3.140, 14.2, 31.4, 55, 75
B: $\frac{2}{5}, \frac{3}{5}, \frac{9}{8}, \frac{8}{7}, \frac{3}{2}, \frac{5}{3}$
C: 0.2, 0.5, 0.6, 0.75, 1, 1.5

32. Check students' number lines.

a. 350 miles east of Omaha or 120 miles west of Chicago; 50 mi/h $\times$ 7 h = 350 mi

b. 225 miles west of Omaha or 275 miles east of Cheyenne; -50 mi/h $\times$ 4.5 h = -225 mi

c. 600 miles west of Omaha or 100 miles west of Cheyenne; 50 mi/h $\times$ (−12 h) = −600 mi

d. 550 miles east of Omaha or 80 miles east of Chicago; −50 mi/h $\times$ (−11 h) = 550 mi

33. a. $[1 + (-3)] \times (-4) = 8$

b. none needed

c. $-6 \div [-2 + (-4)] = 1$

d. none needed

e. none needed

f. $-4 \times (2 - 10) = 32$

34. No, it does not make a difference.
$0.05 \times (7.99 + 3.99) =$
$(0.05 \times 7.99) + (0.05 \times 3.99)$
This is because of the Distributive Property.

35. $4 \times 5 = (4 \times 3) + (4 \times 2)$

Extensions

36. $-23 > -45$

37. $-23 + 10 > -45 + 10$

38. $-23 - 10 > -45 - 10$

39. $-23 \times 10 > -45 \times 10$

40. $-23 \times (-10) < -45 \times (-10)$

41–43. See below for examples.

41. $a + c > b + c$

42. $a - c > b - c$

43. $a \times c > b \times c$ if c is positive
$a \times c < b \times c$ if c is negative
$a \times c = b \times c$ if $c = 0$

Examples:
$$4 > 2$$
$$4 + 3 > 2 + 3$$
$$4 - 3 > 2 - 3$$
$$4 \times 3 > 2 \times 3$$
$$4 \times (-3) < 2 \times -3$$
$$2 > -1$$
$$2 + 1 > -1 + 1$$
$$2 - 1 > -1 - 1$$
$$2 \times 1 > -1 \times 1$$
$$2 \times (-1) < -1 \times (-1)$$

44. a. $n = -12$

b. $n = -4$

c. $n = -4$

45. a. $12 \div (-8 + 4) = -3$
$[12 \div (-8)] + (12 \div 4) = 1.5$

b. $-12 \div [-5 - (-3)] = 6$
$[-12 \div (-5)] - [-12 \div (-3)] = -1.6$

c. $4 \div (-2 - 6) = -0.5$
$(4 \div -2) - (4 \div 6) = -2.67$

d. $3 \div (5 + 6) = 0.2727$
$(3 \div 5) + (3 \div 6) = 1.1$

e. Division does not distribute over addition or subtraction.

46. a. The addition is commutative, but the division is not. For example:
$(10 + 15) \div 2 = 12.5; (15 + 10) \div 2 = 12.5;$
$(6 + 20) \div 2 = 13; (20 + 6) \div 2 = 13;$
addition is commutative, but you must do the addition first, then divide by 2. You cannot do $2 \div (6 + 20)$.

b. Yes, multiplication does distribute over the averaging operation. For example, let $a = 2$, $x = 4$, and $y = 6$; $2(4$ ave $6) = 2[(4 + 6) \div 2] = 2 (5) = 10; (2 \times 4)$ ave $(2 \times 6) = 8$ ave $12 = (8 + 12) \div 2 = 20 \div 2 = 10. 10 = 10$

Possible Answers to Mathematical Reflections

1. a. Order of operations rules make it possible to determine the order in which computations should be done to get the correct answer to a question. Without the order of operations agreements, computation problems may lead to more than one possible answer. These rules bring clarity to the "syntax" of computation.

b. The expression $8 \times (-2) - 4 \div 2$ using the order of operations is -18. With parentheses, the expression $8 \times (-2) - 4 \div 2$ can take on a different meaning and sequence of computations. For example, $8 \times (-2 - 4) \div 2 = -24$.

2. a. *Commutative* means that you can change the order of two adjacent numbers in an expression and it will not change the answer to the computation.

b. Addition is commutative, and subtraction is not. For example, the expressions $-2 + 4$ and $4 + (-2)$ are equivalent. They both have an answer of 2. However, $-2 - 4$ and $4 - (-2)$ are different. The first gives -6, and the second gives 6. Multiplication is commutative, and division is not. For example, $-2 \times 4 = 4 \times (-2) = -8$, but $-2 \div 4 \neq 4 \div (-2)$. The first quotient equals $-\frac{1}{2}$, and the second equals -2.

3. It means that a product of a number N and an expression containing sums and differences can be rewritten as an expression with N multiplied by each number in the parentheses with the sign between the products the same as in the original expression. For example, the expression $N(A + B - C)$ can be rewritten by distributing the factor N over each term of the sums and differences to get $NA + NB - NC$. With numbers we could write: $4(-2 - 5 + 3)$ $= 4 \times (-2) - (4 \times 5) + (4 \times 3)$

Answers to Looking Back and Looking Ahead

1. **a.** 200; answered a 250-point question incorrectly, a 100-point question incorrectly, a 200-point question correctly, and a 200-point question correctly for a total score of 50.
   b. −200; answered a 450-point question correctly, a 250-point question incorrectly, and a 200-point question incorrectly for a total score of 0.
   c. −350; answered a 350-point question incorrectly, a 50-point question correctly, a 200-point question correctly, and a 150-point question incorrectly for a total score of −250.
   d. −200; answered a 350-point question correctly, a 300-point question incorrectly, and a 200-point question incorrectly for a total score of −150.

2. 148 mi

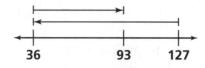

3. **a.** **i.** $-2\frac{1}{2} + n = -3\frac{3}{4}; n - 2\frac{1}{2} = -3\frac{3}{4};$
   $-3\frac{3}{4} - (-2\frac{1}{2}) = n$ or $-3\frac{3}{4} + 2\frac{1}{2} = n;$
   $-3\frac{3}{4} - n = -2\frac{1}{2}$
   ii. $\frac{2}{3}n = 10; n \cdot (\frac{2}{3}) = 10; n = 10 \div \frac{2}{3}$ or
   $n = 10 \times \frac{3}{2}; \frac{2}{3} = 10 \div n$ or $\frac{2}{3} = \frac{10}{n}$

b. For part (i), use $-3\frac{3}{4} + 2\frac{1}{2} = n$. For part (ii), use $n = 10 \div \frac{2}{3}$ or $n = 10 \times \frac{3}{2}$. These are the easiest to solve because they are both represented in terms of n.
   c. $n = -1\frac{1}{4}; n = 15$

4. **a.** See coordinate grid below. $(5, 2)$ is in Quadrant I.
   b. **i.** $(-5, 2)$
   ii. $(-5, -2)$
   iii. $(5, -2)$
   c. These points form a 10 unit × 4 unit rectangle. See coordinate grid below.

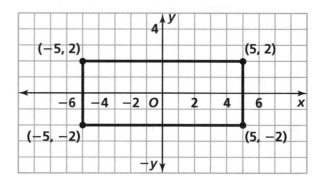

d. A similar figure that is four times as large would have a scale factor of 2 from the original to the image. It would have as vertices $(10, 4), (-10, 4), (-10, -4)$, and $(10, -4)$.

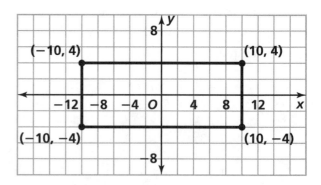

5. When you take the positive number line and flip it over the zero point to get the negative numbers and make marks and labels on the left side of zero to match the marks on the right side, you can see that each negative number is paired with a positive number the same distance from zero on the other side of the number line.

6. a. −20 is greater than −35, since −20 lies to the right of −35 on the number line. Also, since 35 is further to the right from 0 than 20, −35 is further to the left from 0 than −20.

b. $-2\frac{1}{3}$ is greater than $-2\frac{3}{4}$, since $-2\frac{1}{3}$ lies to the right of $-2\frac{3}{4}$ on the number line.

c. 10.5 is greater than −12.5, since 10.5 lies to the right of −12.5 on the number line. Also, 10.5 is positive, while −12.5 is negative.

7. Students may use either model to demonstrate these calculations.

a.

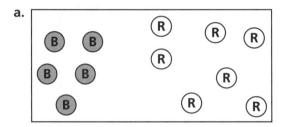

b.

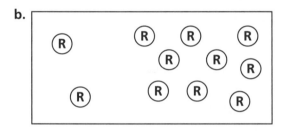

c. Using the time and motion number line model, if Toni is running 2 meters per second to the left, where will she be in 3 seconds?

d. Using the time and motion number line model, if Kumiah passes 0 running 2 meters per second to the left, where was she 3 seconds ago?

e. Addition: −2 + 3

Number Line: Start at −2. Draw an arrow 3 units to the right. End at 1. −2 + 3 = 1
Chip Model: Place 2 red chips on a chip board. Add 3 black chips. Simplify the board by removing red-black (opposites) pairs of chips. 1 black chip remains, so −2 + 3 = 1.

Multiplication: 3 × (−4)

Number Line: 3 × (−4) can be thought of as 3 groups of −4, or −4 + (−4) + (−4). Start at −4 on the number line. Draw an arrow to the left 4 units to represent another −4. Draw another arrow from there to the left 4 units to represent the

last −4. This arrow ends at −12, so 3 × (−4) = −12.
Chip Model: 3 × (−4) is 3 groups of −4, so show 3 groups of 4 red chips, which is −12.

8. a. If both numbers are positive, simply find the sum. If both numbers are negative, find the sum of the absolute values and assign a negative sign. If one number is positive and one number is negative, find the difference of absolute values of the two numbers and take the sign of the number with the greater absolute value.

b. If both numbers are positive, find the difference between the two absolute values. If the first number is greater than the second number, the difference will be positive. If the first number is less than the second number, the difference will be negative. If the first number is positive and the second number is negative, find the absolute sum of the two numbers. The answer will be positive. If the first number is negative and the second number is positive, find the absolute sum of the two numbers. The answer will be negative. If both numbers are negative, you can rewrite the problem as an addition problem. For example, −5 − (−3) = −2 is equivalent to −5 + 3 = −2.

c. Multiply the absolute values of the numbers. The product of two positive numbers is positive. The product of two negative numbers is positive. The product of a positive number and a negative number is negative.

d. Divide the absolute values of the numbers. The quotient of two positive numbers is positive. The quotient of two negative numbers is positive. The quotient of a positive number and a negative number is negative.

9. a. Addition and multiplication are commutative operations.

3 + 4 = 4 + 3
3 × (−4) = −4 × 3

b. Multiplication distributes over addition and subtraction.

4 × (3 + 2) = (4 × 3) + (4 × 2)
4 × (3 − 2) = (4 × 3) − (4 × 2)

Assigning the Unit Project

The optional unit project, *Dealing Down*, allows students to apply what they have learned about operating with integers, using the Distributive and Commutative Properties, and applying the order of operations to make computational sequences clear.

The project has two parts. First, students play a game where they find the least quantity using four number cards drawn from a set. After playing a few rounds of the game, students write a report explaining their strategies for the game and their use of the mathematics of the unit to write an expression for the least possible quantity.

The Labsheets for the number cards and the score sheet appear on pages 117 and 118. A general scoring rubric such as the one below can be used when assessing the project. A teacher's comments on the project and samples of student projects appear after the rubric.

Grading the Unit Project

Suggested Scoring Rubric

This rubric for scoring the *Dealing Down Accentuate the Negative* Project employs a scale that runs from 0 to 4, with a 4+ for work that goes beyond what has been asked for in some unique way. You may use this rubric as presented here or modify it to fit your district's requirements for evaluating and reporting students' work and understanding.

4+ EXEMPLARY RESPONSE

- Complete, with clear, coherent work and written explanations
- Shows understanding of the mathematical concepts and procedures
- Satisfies all essential conditions of the project and goes beyond what is asked for in some unique way

4 COMPLETE RESPONSE

- Complete, with clear, coherent work and written explanations
- Shows understanding of the mathematical concepts and procedures
- Satisfies all essential conditions of the project

3 REASONABLY COMPLETE RESPONSE

- Reasonably complete; may lack detail or clarity in work or written explanations
- Shows understanding of most of the mathematical concepts and procedures
- Satisfies most of the essential conditions of the project

2 PARTIAL RESPONSE

- Incomplete; work or written explanation is unclear or lacks detail
- Shows some understanding of the mathematical concepts and procedures
- Satisfies some of the essential conditions of the project

1 INADEQUATE RESPONSE

- Incomplete; work or written explanation is insufficient or not understandable
- Shows little understanding of the mathematical concepts and procedures
- Fails to address essential conditions of project

0 NO ATTEMPT

Samples of Student Projects

An Example of a Teacher's Specification for the Assignment

Goals

- Write a report explaining strategies for writing the least quantity using four numbers
- Apply concepts learned in *Accentuate the Negative*
- Work toward quality level 4 or above on a 4-level rubric
- Practice expository writing and typing a report on the computer

Criteria and Procedures

- Title—"Dealing Down Report"
- Typed report using size 12 or 14 font
- Introductory paragraph with a topic sentence
- Four detailed supporting paragraphs
  1. Operating with positive and negative numbers
  2. Order of operations
  3. Commutative Property of addition and multiplication
  4. Distributive Property of multiplication over addition and subtraction
- Concluding paragraph
- Paragraphs include mathematical examples
- Use correct mathematical vocabulary
- Use correct conventions
- Name on paper
- In writing your report, focus on creative thinking behaviors such as fluency, originality, elaboration, curiosity, and imagination.

Reflection

- What did you learn from playing the game and doing the report?

Teacher Reflection on the Reports

Four mathematical issues that many students were struggling with became obvious to me while reading the reports.

First: It is important that students know how to interpret exponential notation with negatives. I did not assign the ACE question that would have helped them understand how to interpret -5^4. All of my students assumed incorrectly that this meant: $-5 \cdot (-5) \cdot (-5) \cdot (-5) = 625$. For this year, I will have to revisit the notation, so that my students will know that $-5^4 = -(5 \cdot 5 \cdot 5 \cdot 5) = -625$. In future years, I will make sure that I assign the ACE question and discuss it before doing the project.

Second: If students are using exponents, they may encounter scientific notation on the calculators. It is important to make sure that they understand how to interpret that notation.

Third: At this time, much of the mathematical notation is new to students. With their fragile knowledge and the limitations of assigning them to write the reports on the computer, students often did not communicate expressions accurately. For example, one student wrote $-10/1/3$ (which is equal to $-10 \div 1 \div 3 = 3\frac{1}{3}$). He meant $-10 \div \frac{1}{3} = -30$. I cannot tell if having to type on the computer or his knowledge of the notation caused him to notate the expression incorrectly. Next year, I may have students write the report by hand so I can see their notation without the limitations of the computer.

Fourth: Many students had trouble describing the least quantity. They often wrote something like, "The biggest negative number is the least number." I will need to help them express quantities in terms of the absolute value or in some other reasonable way.

I would have liked students to write more about the strategies that they used while playing the game. I think that my 'Criteria and Procedures' made students focus more on the four detailed supporting paragraphs than on the goal of explaining strategies. In the future, I will revise the 'Criteria and Procedures' to help students focus more on the goals of the written report.

Also, this was the first time doing the project. So, I did not create the rubric until after students had written the report. In the future, I will give students my rubric before they write to help them understand my expectations.

Teacher Reflection on the Game

As I observed students playing the game, I thought of many ways to adapt the game to change the results of how students might form expressions. Here are some ideas that I will try in the future:

- Play a few rounds without using exponents to let students practice computation without calculators.
- Begin playing with 3 cards, then move to 4 cards.
- Play with 5 cards instead of 4.
- Have two students work together against two other students.

- Change the game or the rounds to "Dealing Up" (find the greatest quantity), "Dealing Odd"(find an odd quantity), "Dealing Even" (find an even quantity), "Dealing Down Positive" (find the least positive quantity)

All of the variations will allow me to challenge my students in different ways.

Teacher Grading and Student Work Examples

I used this rubric to help me assess each report and to align it with our district's expectations (see next page).

	Exemplary 4 Complete -Shows understanding of mathematical concepts & procedures -Complete, clear, coherent explanation	Proficient 3 Reasonably Complete -Shows understanding of *most* mathematical concepts & procedures -Lacks detail or clarity	Basic 2 Partial -Shows *some* understanding of mathematical concepts & procedures -Explanation is unclear or lacks detail	Novice 1 Inadequate -Shows *little* understanding of mathematical concepts & procedures -Explanation is insufficient or not understandable	0 No Attempt
Operations with Positive and Negative Numbers					
Order of Operations					
Commutative Property					
Distributive Property					
Explained Strategies					
Criteria and Procedures					

Grading Scale
24 points → A+
23–21 points → A
20–18 points → B
17–15 points → C
14–11 points → D
10 or less points → Revise

Sample

Chadd
4/12/2004

Dealing Down Report

After finishing the math book "Accentuate the Negative" We played dealing down which dealt with integers and rational numbers. The object of the game was to get the smallest numeral possible in each of the five rounds. To do this you would use addition, subtraction, multiplication, division, exponents, and parentheses, to make an equation which equals the smallest number possible. At the start a round one of the three or four people playing draw four cards from an envelope, and place them where everyone can see. Once all of the cards are put down, you may start finding an equation. If your number is the smallest for the round you win a point, and the one with the most points at the end of the game wins. After playing this game myself I found some strategies to win, even though I didn't.

At the start of the first round the numbers dealt were; –1/2, –5, –10, and 1/3. The numerals were a bit tougher then some of the other rounds, since they weren't all integers. Another factor which made this round harder was that there were no exponents, available to use, since you cannot use negatives as exponents, in the game. The next thing to do would be to just find the best order and operations possible to get the smallest number. Firstly we all multiplied –1/2*–5 to make it a positive number 2.5. This was the best move to do, even though it made it a bigger number, because of the next move, we all did. We then multiplied 2.5*–10, to make it the smallest number possible, because when multiplying

by doing 10/9 than 1*–1. Then, there are only 1 and –1 which would do nothing to make your problem smaller if you multiplied or divided them so all of us used the rules we knew when adding and subtracting numbers when you are dealing with negatives. First (it doesn't matter what order you do it in) all of us took –90+–1, and got –91, because whenever adding negatives to a negative the number is always smaller. The we took –91–1 so we get –92, because when subtracting a positive from a negative you always get a smaller number, having us all win in round two, for the final equation to be 9*10+–1–1=–92, but it wasn't like this in round 3.

At the start of the third round the numbers dealt were; 8, 2, 5, and –5. At the beginning of the round everyone saw the simplest move. -8^5, this would obviously make the number much smaller, because multiplying –8*–8*–8*–8*–8. The answer comes up to be –32,768. Any other exponents would be to use -5^2, which would be to make the number bigger and thought not to use it, and you could use –5 as an exponent since you can't use negatives as exponents in this game. So, Taylor and I just took –32,768 and multiplied it by 2, to get –65,572, because when multiplying a negative by a positive you always get a negative. Then, with the 5 we just subtracted it so we could get for our final answer –65,577. Matthew though took an entirely different approach. Firstly, he took the –5 to the second power (5^2) something that we thought would be horrible since you get 25, but he did something we never thought of. After doing that he took the –32,768 and multiplied it to the 25, and since your multiplying a positive

a positive to a negative the outcome comes out negative, which in this case was –25, the biggest number possible. The move is how Taylor (another person playing the game) won the game. Instead of just subtracting it to make it smaller she divided it. Normally when you take a positive numeral divided by a fraction the number would actually be bigger, but when using a negative divided by a positive it's the exact opposite. So, when taking –25/1/3 you get –75, using all the numbers, and making the final equation –1/2*–5*–10/1/3=–75 the smallest number, which leads me on to the next round where Matthew, and I were more successful.

At the start of the second round the numbers dealt were; 1, –1, 10, and –9. In this one you can use the 10 as an exponent, but it will make a much number bigger, because when you have a negative number and an even exponent the number will end up positive, but if you have the same situation, except with an odd exponent the number will be negative. For example, if you use -9^{10} the answer would end up being 3,486,784,401, and with numbers such as 1 and –1 there is no way you would even get it close to a negative number. After that the next obvious thing would to do would be to multiply 10*–9, to get –90, which gives you the smallest number, for the start. You could also do –9*10, because of the commutative property, which means that it doesn't matter what order you put the numbers in an addition or multiplication problem you will always get the same answer. The only other way to multiply so you can be in the negatives would be to take 1*–1 to get only –1 a way bigger. You could actually get a bigger number

by a negative the answer comes out way smaller. The answer ended up being 819,200 with the final equation being –85*52=–819,200, and in round 3 Matthew ends up being more creative.

At the start of the fourth round the numbers dealt were; –2, –9, –10, and 5. In this one the other obvious move was to take –10 to the 5th power (-10^5) and get –100,000. After that Taylor and I try to make the number even smaller multiplied –9*–2 to get 18, and we used that so we could use that number to multiply it by 100,000 so it's smaller. How we did this was set up and equation that looks like this 10^5 (–9*–2) the answer ends up being –1,800,000. We could do that, because of the order of operations. This means no matter where you the number is in the problem you have to do it if it's one of the first things on the rules. The rules are; 1.Do whatever is inside parentheses first. 2. Do any exponents. 3. Do any multiplication or division. 4. Do any addition or subtraction. Note: If there is more than one type of that in the order go left to right. So, how ours worked is, because you do what's in the parentheses first. In our case –9*–2 was in the parentheses and –9*–2 = –18, so you have that part of the problem done. There is also an exponent in our problem so you take the 10^5 after that to get 100,000. Then you do the multiplication or division, and there is some multiplication you just might not recognize it. Whenever there is a number outside the parentheses you multiply it to the number which was in it, because) or (also means multiplication. So, for the final answer you take 18*–100,000 to get –1,800,000. Matthew also used parentheses, but in an entirely different way. Instead

Sample

Matthew's equation looked like this; $(-2*-10*-9)^5$ which makes a really small number. First you do what's inside the parentheses, which is $-2*-10*-9$ and equals, 180. You then take -180 to the 5th power. The number comes out being $-189,000,000,000$ with the equation being $(-2*10*9)^5 = -189,000,000,000$, but Matthew doesn't come up so creative in round 5.

At the start of the 5th round the numbers dealt were; $-4, 0, 3,$ and 0.5. With these numbers you really can't make them that small, but there is one possible exponent that can be used with another number to make a small one. Everyone one in the group saw it, -4^3. No other numbers would be impossible to use because there is 0.5, and 0. -4 to the 3rd power is -64, the next move is how Taylor and I won the game with the same strategy used in round 1. We took $-64/0.5$ which normally if either positive or, both negative would make the numeral bigger, but since one is positive and the other is negative the exact opposite happens, making the answer -128. Then the only thing to do with the zero would be to add or subtract to make the number same for the final answer being -128, and the final equation being $-4^3/0.5+0=-128$, and the ending the last round of Dealing Down.

Dealing Down is a really good game for working with negatives and using creative ideas to try to get the smallest numbers. After you playing you can learn better strategies which improve your game, and of course you get a better understanding about negatives.

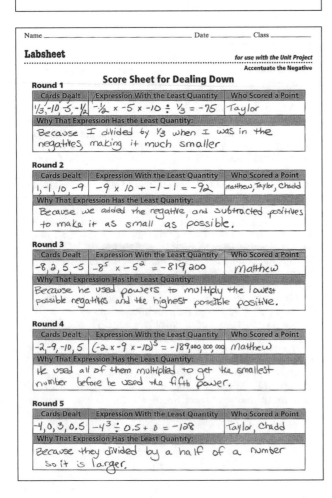

A Teacher's Comments on Sample 1

Chadd's report was the most unique of my students. His paper communicated to me the mathematics he used from the unit while playing the game. He explains each round of the game, the decisions that his group members made, and how they operated with rational numbers, used the order of operations, and the Commutative Property. He does not explain the Distributive Property. No one used it when playing the game.

He is one of the few students in the class that described the strategies used while playing the game. I liked this way of reporting. It really gave me a view of how the students in the group reasoned about the numbers to impact the quantity of their final expression.

The style and completeness of his report gave me more insight into the mathematical reasoning that he and his group members had. For example, he knows that integers do not include fractions. He knows some things about fraction operations.

He has incorrectly notated -8^5 to mean $-8 \times (-8) \times (-8) \times (-8) \times (-8)$. This brought to my attention that others in the class had this same misunderstanding. I gave him 3 points for order of operations to bring this to his attention.

Also, he received 2 points for the Distributive Property. It was part of the assignment to explain it, but he interpreted the assignment as explaining through their strategies, so I could not give him a 0. Overall, he received 21 points.

The next time I do this project, I will use Chadd's report as an example of one way to write about strategies. I will also show examples from parts of other reports where students showed they used concepts with examples from the game. I will also have to decide if it is necessary for students to describe every major concept from the unit or how they use the concepts in the game. Most students did the former. Chadd did the latter and it showed me more about his ability to use the mathematics from the unit.

The student edition pages for this
investigation begin on the next page.

Notes _____
_____
_____
_____

Unit Project

Dealing Down

Dealing Down is a mathematics card game that tests your creative skill at writing expressions. Play several rounds of the game. Then write a report on the strategies you found.

How to Play Dealing Down

- Work in small groups.
- Shuffle the 25 cards marked with the following numbers.
  $-10, -9, -8, -7, -6, -5, -4, -3, -2, -1, -\frac{1}{2}, -\frac{1}{3}, -\frac{1}{4}, 0,$
  $0.25, \frac{1}{3}, 0.5, 1, 2, 3, 4, 5, 7, 8, 10$
- Deal four cards to the center of the table.
- All players use the four numbers to write an expression with the least possible quantity.
- Players compare answers and discuss how they know their quantity is accurate and the least possible.
- Each player with an expression for the least quantity gets 1 point.
- Record the results of that round in a table like the one below and play more rounds.

Round 1

Cards Dealt	Expression With the Least Quantity	Who Scored a Point
Why That Expression Has the Least Quantity:		

- The player with the most points at the end of the game wins.

Notes _____

_____

_____

_____

Write a Report

Write a report about strategies for writing the least possible quantity using four numbers.

Consider the following ideas as you look at the strategies in Dealing Down.

- Operating with negative and positive numbers
- Order of operations including the use of parentheses and exponents
- Commutative Property of Addition and Multiplication
- Distributive Property

Unit Project Dealing Down   **77**

Notes _____

_____

_____

_____

Looking Back and Looking Ahead

Unit Review

In this unit, you investigated properties, operations, and applications of integers. You learned how to

Go Online
PHSchool.com
For: Vocabulary Review Puzzle
Web Code: anj-4051

- Add, subtract, multiply and divide with integers
- Represent integers and operations on a chip board and a number line
- Use integers in real-world problems

Use Your Understanding: Integers and Rational Numbers

Test your understanding of integers by solving the following problems.

1. An absent-minded scorekeeper writes the number sentences below. Find the value of n that makes each sentence true. Explain what each sentence tells about the rounds of play.

   a. BrainyActs: $-250 + (-100) + 200 + n = 50$

   b. MathXperts: $450 + (-250) + n = 0$

   c. ExCells: $n + 50 + 200 + (-150) = -250$

   d. SuperM's: $350 + (-300) + n = -150$

2. Irving goes to college 127 miles away from home. When he drives home for vacation, he plans to drop off his friend, Whitney, along the way. Her exit is 93 miles before his exit,

   Irving and Whitney are so busy talking that they miss the exit to her house. They are now only 36 miles from Irving's exit! How far do they have to travel in all from college until they finally reach Whitney's exit? Model this problem on a number line.

3. **a.** Write a fact family for each sentence.

   i. $-2\frac{1}{2} + n = -3\frac{3}{4}$ **ii.** $\frac{2}{3}n = 10$

   b. Which member of each fact family would make it easy to solve for n? Explain.

   c. Find the value for n that makes each sentence true.

Notes _____

_____

_____

_____

4. **a.** Locate point $(5, 2)$ on a coordinate grid.

   b. Find a related point in each quadrant by changing the sign of one or both coordinates.

      i. Quadrant II   **ii.** Quadrant III   **iii.** Quadrant IV

   c. Connect these points in order. Describe the figure formed.

   d. Make a similar figure with an area four times as large and that has a vertex in each quadrant. Give the four vertices as ordered pairs.

Explain Your Reasoning

Answer the following questions to summarize what you know now.

5. Describe what a number line looks like now that the number system has been extended to include negative numbers.

6. Which number is greater? Explain.

   a. $-20, -35$ **b.** $-2\frac{3}{4}, -2\frac{1}{3}$ **c.** $-12.5, 10.5$

7. Use a number line or chip model to check each calculation. Show your work.

   a. $5 + (-7) = -2$ **b.** $-2 + (-9) = -11$

   c. $3 \times (-2) = -6$ **d.** $-3 \times (-2) = 6$

   e. Describe how a number line and chip model can be used to model an addition or multiplication problem.

8. Suppose you are given two integers. How do you find their

   a. sum?   **b.** difference?

   c. product?   **d.** quotient?

9. Which operations with integers have the following properties? Give numerical examples.

   a. commutative   **b.** distributive

Look Ahead

Positive and negative numbers are useful in solving a variety of problems that involve losses and gains. They also provide coordinates for points on an extended number line and coordinate plane. These ideas will be useful when you study graphs of functions and solve equations in future *Connected Mathematics* units such as *Moving Straight Ahead*, *Thinking With Mathematical Models*, *Say It With Symbols*, and *The Shapes of Algebra*.

Notes _____

_____

_____

_____

A

absolute value The absolute value of a number is its distance from 0 on a number line. It can be thought of as the value of a number when its sign is ignored. For example, −3 and 3 both have an absolute value of 3.

valor absoluto El valor absoluto de un número es su distancia de 0 sobre una recta numérica. Se puede interpretar como el valor de un número cuando no importa su signo. Por ejemplo, tanto −3 como 3 tienen un valor absoluto de 3.

algorithm A set of rules for performing a procedure. Mathematicians invent algorithms that are useful in many kinds of situations. Some examples of algorithms are the rules for long division or the rules for adding two fractions.

algoritmo Un conjunto de reglas para realizar un procedimiento. Los matemáticos inventan algoritmos que son útiles en muchos tipos de situaciones. Algunos ejemplos de algoritmos son las reglas para una división larga o las reglas para sumar dos fracciones.

Associative Property Allows addends or factors to be grouped and computed in different arrangements. For example, 2 + 3 + 5 can be grouped as (2 + 3) + 5 or 2 + (3 + 5). So, (2 + 3) + 5 = 5 + 5 = 10 and 2 + (3 + 5) = 2 + 8 = 10. This property does not work for subtraction or division. For example, 8 − (4 − 2) ≠ (8 − 4) − 2 and 8 ÷ (4 ÷ 2) ≠ (8 ÷ 4) ÷ 2.

propiedad asociativa Permite que sumandos o factores se agrupen y se calculen de diferentes maneras. Por ejemplo, 2 + 3 + 5 se puede agrupar como (2 + 3) + 5 ó 2 + (3 + 5). Por lo tanto, (2 + 3) + 5 = 5 + 5 = 10 y 2 + (3 + 5) = 2 + 8 = 10. Esta propiedad no funciona con la resta o la división. Por ejemplo, 8 − (4 − 2) ≠ (8 − 4) − 2 y 8 ÷ (4 ÷ 2) ≠ (8 ÷ 4) ÷ 2.

C

Commutative Property The order of the addition or multiplication of two numbers does not change the result. For two numbers a and b, $a + b = b + a$, and $a \cdot b = b \cdot a$.

propiedad conmutativa El orden en la suma o multiplicación de dos números no afecta el resultado. Para dos números a y b, $a + b = b + a$, y $a \cdot b = b \cdot a$.

D

Distributive Property The Distributive Property shows how multiplication combines with addition or subtraction. For three numbers a, b, and c, $a(b + c) = ab + ac$.

propiedad distributiva La propiedad distributiva muestra cómo la multiplicación se combina con la suma o la resta. Para tres números a, b y c, $a(b + c) = ab + ac$.

I

integers The whole numbers and their opposites. 0 is an integer, but is neither positive nor negative. The integers from −4 to 4 are shown on the number line below.

enteros Números enteros positivos y sus opuestos. 0 es un entero, pero no es ni positivo ni negativo. En la siguiente recta numérica figuran los enteros comprendidos entre −4 y 4.

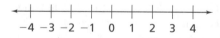

80 Accentuate the Negative

Notes

_____

_____

_____

_____

inverse operations Operations that "undo" each other. Addition and subtraction are inverse operations. For example, start with 7. Subtract 4. Then add 4. You are back to the original number 7. Thus, $7 - 4 + 4 = 7$. Multiplication and division are inverse operations. For example, start with 12. Multiply by 2. Then divide by 2. You are back at the original number 12. Thus, $(12 \times 2) \div 2 = 12$.

operaciones inversas Operaciones que se "anulan" mutuamente. La suma y la resta son operaciones inversas. Por ejemplo, empieza con 7. Resta 4. Luego, suma 4. Tienes otra vez el número 7. Por eso, $7 - 4 + 4 = 7$. La multiplicación y la división son operaciones inversas. Por ejemplo, empieza con 12. Multiplica por 2. Luego, divide por 2. Tienes otra vez el número 12. Por eso, $(12 \times 2) \div 2 = 12$.

N

negative number A number less than 0. On a number line, negative numbers are located to the left of 0 (on a vertical number line, negative numbers are located below 0).

número negativo Un número menor que 0. En una recta numérica, los números negativos están ubicados a la izquierda del 0 (en una recta numérica vertical, los números negativos están ubicados debajo del 0).

number sentence A mathematical statement that gives the relationship between two expressions that are composed of numbers and operation signs. For example, $3 + 2 = 5$ and $6 \times 2 > 10$ are number sentences; $3 + 2, 5, 6 \times 2$, and 10 are expressions.

oración numérica Un enunciado matemático que describe la relación entre dos expresiones compuestas por números y signos de operaciones. Por ejemplo, $3 + 2 = 5$ y $6 \times 2 > 10$ son oraciones numéricas. $3 + 2, 5, 6 \times 2$ y 10 son expresiones.

O

opposites Two numbers whose sum is 0. For example, -3 and 3 are opposites. On a number line, opposites are the same distance from 0 but in different directions from 0. The number 0 is its own opposite.

opuestos Dos números cuya suma da 0. Por ejemplo, -3 y 3 son opuestos. En una recta numérica, los opuestos se encuentran a la misma distancia de 0 pero en distintos sentidos. El número 0 es su propio opuesto.

order of operations Established order in which to perform mathematical operations.
1. Compute any expressions within parentheses.
2. Compute any exponents.
3. Multiply and divide in order from left to right.
4. Add and subtract in order from left to right.

orden de operaciones Orden establecido en el cual se deben realizar las operacíones matemáticas.
1. Calcular cualquier expresión dentro del paréntesis.
2. Calcular cualquier exponente.
3. Multiplicar y dividir de izquierda a derecha.
4. Sumar y restar de izquierda a derecha.

P

positive number A number greater than 0. (The number 0 is neither positive nor negative.) On a number line, positive numbers are located to the right of 0 (on a vertical number line, positive numbers are located above 0).

número positivo Un número mayor que 0. (El número 0 no es ni positivo ni negativo.) En una recta numérica, los números positivos se ubican a la derecha del 0 (en una recta numérica vertical, los números positivos están por encima del 0).

English/Spanish Glossary   **81**

Notes

quadrants The four sections into which the coordinate plane is divided by the *x*- and *y*-axes. The quadrants are labeled as follows:

cuadrantes Las cuatro secciones en las que un plano de coordenadas queda dividido por los ejes *x* e *y*. Los cuadrantes se identifican de la siguiente manera:

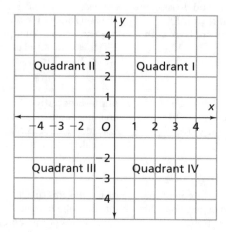

R

rational numbers Numbers that can be expressed as a quotient of two integers where the divisor is not zero. For example, $\frac{1}{2}$, $\frac{9}{11}$, and $-\frac{7}{5}$ are rational numbers. Also, 0.799 is a rational number, since $0.799 = \frac{799}{1,000}$.

números racionales Números que se pueden expresar como un cociente de dos números enteros donde el divisor no es cero. Por ejemplo, $\frac{1}{2}$, $\frac{9}{11}$ y $-\frac{7}{5}$ son números racionales. También 0.799 es un número racional, porque $0.799 = \frac{799}{1,000}$.

82   Accentuate the Negative

Notes

Academic Vocabulary

Academic vocabulary words are words that you see in textbooks and on tests. These are not math vocabulary terms, but knowing them will help you succeed in mathematics.

Las palabras de vocabulario académico son palabras que ves en los libros de texto y en las pruebas. Éstos no son términos de vocabulario de matemáticas, pero conocerlos te ayudará a tener éxito en matemáticas.

D

describe To explain or tell in detail. A written description can contain facts and other information needed to communicate your answer. A diagram or a graph may also be included.
related terms: express, explain

Sample: Given the pair of points ($^+$5, $^+$7) and ($^-$4, $^+$7), describe the direction and the distance between the first point and the second point on a coordinate graph.

> The direction from ($^+$5, $^+$7) to ($^-$4, $^+$7) is to the left. The distance between the two points is the distance between the x-coordinates because the y-coordinates are the same. The distance between the x-coordinates is the distance from $^+$5 to the y-axis plus the distance from the y-axis to $^-$4: $5 + 4 = 9$.

describir Explicar o decir con detalles. Una descripción escrita puede tener datos e información necesaria para comunicar tu respuesta. También puedes incluir un diagrama o una gráfica.
términos relacionados: expresar, explicar

Ejemplo: Dados los pares de puntos ($^+$5, $^+$7) y ($^-$4, $^+$7), describe la dirección y la distancia entre el primer punto y el segundo punto de un plano de coordenadas.

> La dirección desde ($^+$5, $^+$7) a ($^-$4, $^+$7) es hacia la izquierda. La distancia entre los dos puntos es la distancia entre las coordenadas x, porque las coordenadas y son iguales. La distancia entre las coordenadas x es la distancia desde $^+$5 al eje de y más la distancia del eje de y a $^-$4: $5 + 4 = 9$.

E

explain To give facts and details that make an idea easier to understand. Explaining can involve a written summary supported by a diagram, chart, table, or a combination of these.
related terms: describe, show, justify, tell, present

Sample: Explain how to multiply two negative numbers.

> To multiply two negative numbers, multiply as if both numbers were positive. The product will be a positive number.

explicar Dar datos y detalles que facilitan el entendimiento de una idea. Explicar puede requerir la preparación de un informe escrito apoyado por un diagrama, una tabla, un esquema o una combinación de éstos.
términos relacionados: describir, mostrar, justificar, decir, presentar

Ejemplo: Explica cómo se multiplican dos números negativos.

> Para multiplicar dos números negativos, multiplica como si ambos números fueran positivos. El producto será un número positivo.

Academic Vocabulary **83**

Notes _____

_____

_____

_____

locate To find or identify a value, usually on a number line or coordinate graph.
related terms: find, identify

Sample: Locate and label the points (⁻3, 4), (⁻3, ⁻4), and (3, 4) on a coordinate graph.

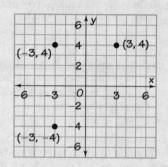

I can draw and label an x and y-axis on grid paper and locate the points.

ubicar Hallar o identificar un valor, generalmente en una recta numérica o en un plano de coordenadas.
términos relacionados: hallar, identificar

Ejemplo: Ubica y rotula los puntos (⁻3, 4), (⁻3, ⁻4), y (3, 4) en un plano de coordenadas.

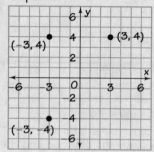

Puedo dibujar y rotular un eje para las x y un eje para las y en el papel cuadriculado, y ubicar los puntos.

R

represent To stand for or take the place of something else. Symbols, equations, charts, and tables are often used to represent particular situations.
related terms: symbolize, stand for

Sample: Players spin a 0–5 spinner and then pick a signed card to see how far and in which direction they will move. Sally started at zero, spun a 5, and picked a negative card. She then spun a 3 and picked a positive card. Which of the following expressions represents her distance from zero on a number line?

A. $|3 + 5|$ **B.** $|{}^-3 - 5|$ **C.** $|{}^-5 + 3|$

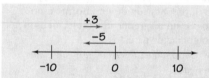

Sally moved five units in a negative direction and then three units in a positive direction. Absolute value signs are used to show distance, so the answer is C.

representar Reemplazar u ocupar el lugar de algo. Para representar situaciones particulares se suelen usar símbolos, ecuaciones, diagramas y tablas.
términos relacionados: simbolizar, significar

Ejemplo: Los jugadores hacen girar una rueda giratoria numerada del 0 al 5 y después sacan una tarjeta para ver qué tanto y en qué dirección se tienen que mover. Sally empezó en el cero, le salió un 5 en la rueda giratoria y sacó una tarjeta negativa. Después le salió un 3 y sacó una tarjeta positiva. ¿Cuál de las siguientes expresiones representa la distancia que recorrió desde el cero en una recta numérica?

A. $|3 + 5|$ **B.** $|{}^-3 - 5|$ **C.** $|{}^-5 + 3|$

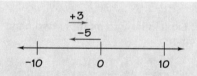

Sally se movió cinco unidades en dirección negativa y después tres unidades en dirección positiva. Para mostrar la distancia se usan signos de valor absoluto, por lo tanto la respuesta es la C.

84   Accentuate the Negative

Notes _____

_____

_____

_____

Index

Index

Notes _____

Notes _____

_____

_____

_____

Acknowledgments

Team Credits

The people who made up the **Connected Mathematics 2** team—representing editorial, editorial services, design services, and production services—are listed below. Bold type denotes core team members.

Leora Adler, Judith Buice, Kerry Cashman, Patrick Culleton, Sheila DeFazio, Katie Hallahan, Richard Heater, **Barbara Hollingdale, Jayne Holman,** Karen Holtzman, **Etta Jacobs,** Christine Lee, Carolyn Lock, Catherine Maglio, **Dotti Marshall,** Rich McMahon, Eve Melnechuk, Kristin Mingrone, Terri Mitchell, **Marsha Novak,** Irene Rubin, Donna Russo, Robin Samper, Siri Schwartzman, **Nancy Smith,** Emily Soltanoff, **Mark Tricca,** Paula Vergith, Roberta Warshaw, Helen Young

Additional Credits

Diana Bonfilio, Mairead Reddin, Michael Torocsik, nSight, Inc.

Technical Illustration

WestWords, Inc.

Cover Design

tom white.images

Photos

2, Richard Haynes; **3,** AP Photo/Jonathan Hayward; **5,** Richard Haynes; **8,** Richard Haynes; **10,** Stephanie Maze/Corbis; **12,** AP Photo/Gregory Smith; **14,** PhotoDisc/Getty Images, Inc.; **17,** Josh Mitchell/Getty Images, Inc.; **22,** Creatas/AGE Fotostock; **28,** Richard Haynes; **37,** Creatas/PictureQuest; **43,** Paul J. Sutton/Corbis; **50,** Dennis MacDonald/PhotoEdit; **53,** Spencer Grant/PhotoEdit; **56,** SuperStock, Inc./SuperStock; **60,** Richard Haynes; **61,** Syracuse Newspapers/The Image Works; **64,** Tom Carter/PhotoEdit; **71,** Dennis MacDonald/Index Stock Imagery, Inc.; **77,** Richard Haynes

Data Sources

Temperature data on page 12 are from Temperatures in Spearfish South Dakota. Source: National Weather Service.

Note: Every effort has been made to locate the copyright owner of the material reprinted in this book. Omissions brought to our attention will be corrected in subsequent editions.

Notes _____
_____
_____
_____

Labsheet 1ACE Exercises 31 and 48

31. Find the value for each labeled point on the number line. Then use the values to calculate each change.

    a. A to B   **b.** A to C   **c.** B to C   **d.** C to A   **e.** B to A

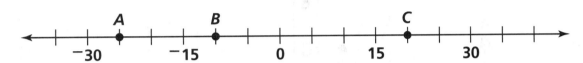

48. At the start of December, Kenji had a balance of $595.50 in his checking account. The following is a list of transactions he made during the month.

Date	Transaction	Balance
December 1		$595.50
December 5	Writes a check for $19.95	
December 12	Writes a check for $280.88	
December 15	Deposits $257.00	
December 17	Writes a check for $58.12	
December 21	Withdraws $50.00	
December 24	Writes checks for $17.50, $41.37, and $65.15	
December 26	Deposits $100.00	
December 31	Withdraws $50.00	

    a. Complete the table.

    b. What was Kenji's balance at the end of December?

    c. When was his balance the greatest?

    d. When was his balance the least?

Labsheet 2.5

Questions C and D

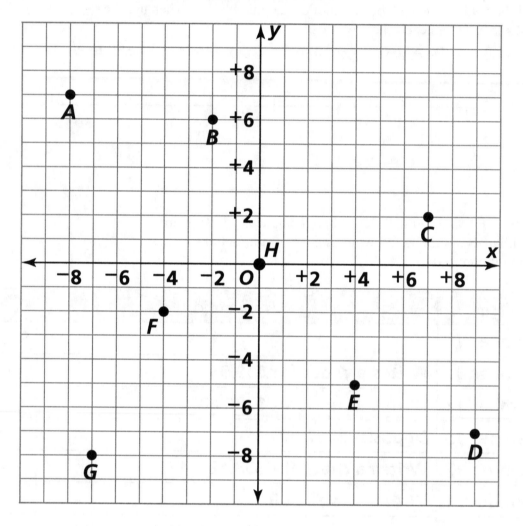

Labsheet 3.4

Integer Product Game Board

−36	−30	−25	−24	−20	−18
−16	−15	−12	−10	−9	−8
−6	−5	−4	−3	−2	−1
1	2	3	4	5	6
8	9	10	12	15	16
18	20	24	25	30	36

Factors:

−6 −5 −4 −3 −2 −1 1 2 3 4 5 6

Integer Product Game Board

−36	−30	−25	−24	−20	−18
−16	−15	−12	−10	−9	−8
−6	−5	−4	−3	−2	−1
1	2	3	4	5	6
8	9	10	12	15	16
18	20	24	25	30	36

Factors:

−6 −5 −4 −3 −2 −1 1 2 3 4 5 6

Labsheet 3ACE Exercise 25 parts (a) and (b)

Coordinates for Mug and Variations

Rule	(x, y)	(2x, 2y)	(−2x, −2y)
Head Outline	(−4, −2)		
	(−2, −2)		
	(−2, −3)		
Nose	(−1, 1)		
Mouth	(−2, −1)		
Eyes	(−2, 2)		

Labsheet 3ACE Exercise 25 parts (c) and (d)

Accentuate the Negative

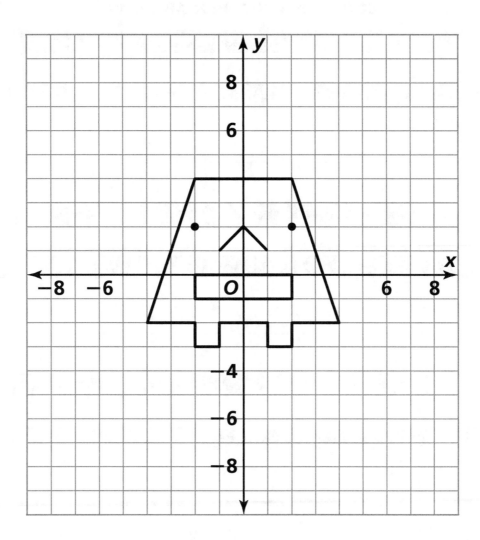

Comparison of Mouths

	Rule	Length	Width	Area
Mug's Mouth	(x, y)			
Mug 2's Mouth	(2x, 2y)			
Mug –2's Mouth	(–2x, –2y)			

Labsheet UP.A

Score Sheet for Dealing Down

Round 1

Cards Dealt	Expression With the Least Quantity	Who Scored a Point

Why That Expression Has the Least Quantity:

Round 2

Cards Dealt	Expression With the Least Quantity	Who Scored a Point

Why That Expression Has the Least Quantity:

Round 3

Cards Dealt	Expression With the Least Quantity	Who Scored a Point

Why That Expression Has the Least Quantity:

Round 4

Cards Dealt	Expression With the Least Quantity	Who Scored a Point

Why That Expression Has the Least Quantity:

Round 5

Cards Dealt	Expression With the Least Quantity	Who Scored a Point

Why That Expression Has the Least Quantity:

Labsheet UP.B

Cards for Dealing Down

0	**−1**	**−2**	**−3**	**−4**
−5	**−6**	**−7**	**−8**	**−9**
$-\dfrac{1}{2}$	$-\dfrac{1}{3}$	$-\dfrac{1}{4}$	**0.5**	$\dfrac{1}{3}$
0.25	**1**	**10**	**5**	**7**
8	**2**	**3**	**4**	**−10**

Number Lines

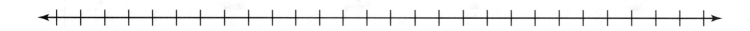

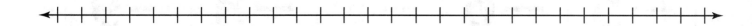

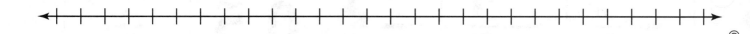

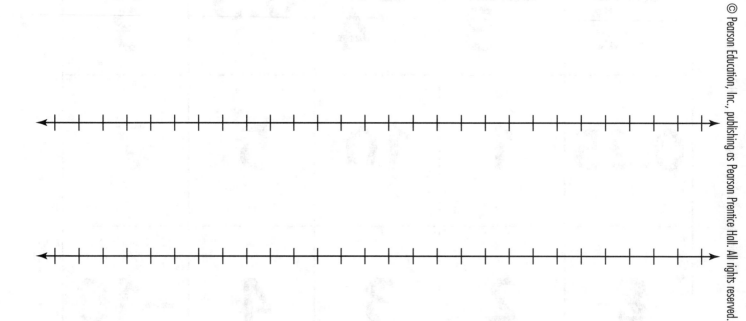

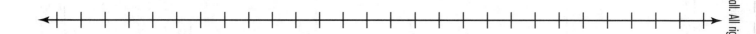

Chip Board

Chip Board

Small Chip Boards

Chip Board

Chip Board

Chip Board

Chip Board

Chip Board

Chip Board

Coordinate Grid

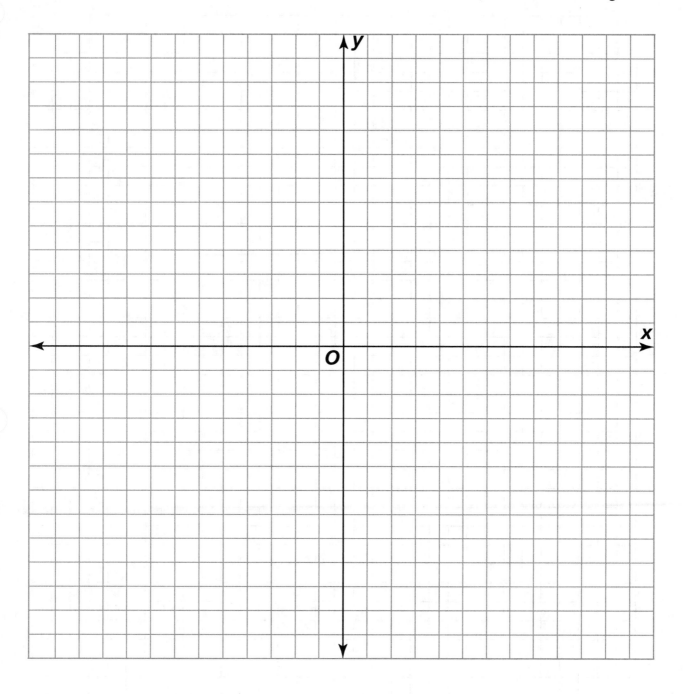

Graph Paper

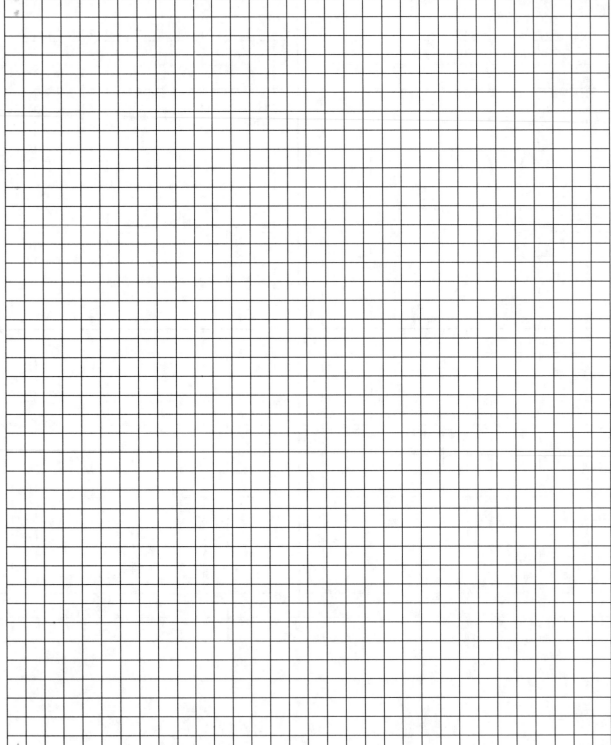

PACING: _____

Mathematical Goals

_____

_____

_____

_____

Launch

_____

_____

_____

_____

_____

_____

_____

Materials

Explore

_____

_____

_____

_____

_____

_____

_____

Materials

Summarize

_____

_____

_____

_____

_____

_____

_____

Materials

Glossary

absolute value The absolute value of a number is its distance from 0 on a number line. It can be thought of as the value of a number when its sign is ignored. For example, −3 and 3 both have an absolute value of 3.

algorithm A set of rules for performing a procedure. Mathematicians develop algorithms that are useful in many kinds of situations. Some examples of algorithms are the rules for long division or the rules for adding two fractions.

Associative Property Allows addends or factors to be grouped and computed in different arrangements. For example, $2 + 3 + 5$ can be grouped as $(2 + 3) + 5$ or $2 + (3 + 5)$. So, $(2 + 3) + 5 = 5 + 5 = 10$ and $2 + (3 + 5) = 2 + 8 = 10$. This property does not work for subtraction or division. For example, $8 − (4 − 2) \neq (8 − 4) − 2$ and $8 \div (4 \div 2) \neq (8 \div 4) \div 2$.

Commutative Property The order of the addition or multiplication of two numbers does not change the result. For two numbers a and b, $a + b = b + a$ and $a \cdot b = b \cdot a$.

Distributive Property The Distributive Property shows how multiplication combines with addition or subtraction. For three numbers a, b, and c, $a(b + c) = ab + ac$.

integers The whole numbers and their opposites. 0 is an integer, but is neither positive nor negative. The integers from −4 to 4 are shown on the number line below.

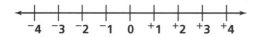

inverse operations Operations that "undo" each other. Addition and subtraction are inverse operations. For example, start with 7. Subtract 4. Then add 4. You are back to the original number 7. Thus, $7 − 4 + 4 = 7$. Multiplication and division are inverse operations. For example, start with 12. Multiply by 2. Then divide by 2. You are back at the original number 12. Thus, $(12 \times 2) \div 2 = 12$.

negative number A number less than 0. On a number line, negative numbers are located to the left of 0 (on a vertical number line, negative numbers are located below 0).

number sentence A mathematical statement that gives the relationship between two expressions that are composed of numbers and operation signs. For example, $3 + 2 = 5$ and $6 \times 2 > 10$ are number sentences; $3 + 2$, 5, 6×2, and 10 are expressions.

opposites Two numbers whose sum is 0. For example, −3 and 3 are opposites. On a number line, opposites are the same distance from 0 but in different directions from 0. The number 0 is its own opposite.

order of operations Established order in which to perform mathematical operations.
1. Compute any expressions within parentheses.
2. Compute any exponents.
3. Multiply and divide in order from left to right.
4. Add and subtract in order from left to right.

positive number A number greater than 0. (The number 0 is neither positive nor negative.) On a number line, positive numbers are located to the right of 0 (on a vertical number line, positive numbers are located above 0).

Q
---

quadrants The four sections into which the coordinate plane is divided by the *x*- and *y*-axes. The quadrants are labeled as follows:

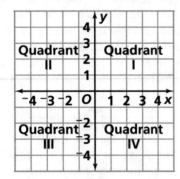

R
---

rational numbers Numbers that can be expressed as a quotient of two integers where the divisor is not zero. For example, $\frac{1}{2}$, $\frac{9}{11}$, and $-\frac{7}{5}$ are rational numbers.

Also, 0.799 is a rational number, since $0.799 = \frac{799}{1,000}$.

Index

Acknowledgments

Team Credits

The people who made up the **Connected Mathematics 2** team—representing editorial, editorial services, design services, and production services—are listed below. Bold type denotes core team members.

Leora Adler, Judith Buice, Kerry Cashman, Patrick Culleton, Sheila DeFazio, Richard Heater, **Barbara Hollingdale, Jayne Holman,** Karen Holtzman, **Etta Jacobs,** Christine Lee, Carolyn Lock, Catherine Maglio, **Dotti Marshall,** Rich McMahon, Eve Melnechuk, Kristin Mingrone, Terri Mitchell, **Marsha Novak,** Irene Rubin, Donna Russo, Robin Samper, Siri Schwartzman, **Nancy Smith,** Emily Soltanoff, **Mark Tricca,** Paula Vergith, Roberta Warshaw, Helen Young

Additional Credits

Diana Bonfilio, Mairead Reddin, Michael Torocsik, nSight, Inc.

Technical Illustration

Schawk, Inc.

Cover Design

tom white.images